AN INTRODUCTION TO DEDUCTIVE LOGIC

THE CENTURY PHILOSOPHY SERIES

Justus Buchler and Sterling P. Lamprecht, *Editors*

AN INTRODUCTION TO
Deductive Logic

GARY ISEMINGER
Carleton College

New York

APPLETON-CENTURY-CROFTS
EDUCATIONAL DIVISION
MEREDITH CORPORATION

for Andrea

PREFACE

This book is distinguished by the following features: (i) it employs a version of Polish notation; (ii) it develops the properties of truth-functional connectives, modalities, and quantifiers mainly through the use of natural deduction techniques, although at the same time it contains developments of the truth-functional propositional calculus by means of truth tables and by means of an axiomatic deductive system in order to facilitate metatheoretic discussion of the calculus and to provide a basis for understanding by contrast the special features of natural deduction techniques; (iii) it sees the logician's job as generally that of capturing and giving a theoretical account of inferences which are in fact normally regarded as valid, and it therefore emphasizes questions concerning the correlation of symbols in formal systems with concepts employed in ordinary discourse; (iv) it attempts to indicate, though not to discuss in detail, the philosophical questions which arise from formal logic as well as those to whose answers and formulations logic has claimed to contribute and to suggest, through notes containing references to my anthology *Logic and Philosophy: Selected Readings* (New York, Appleton-Century-Crofts, 1968) and to the literature, ways in which interested readers may pursue some of these questions.

This book is perhaps shorter than many logic books. I have intentionally compressed rather than expanded my discussions. I have not attempted to pre-empt the teacher's function but rather to give him something he can use as a basis for discussion. My consideration of philosophical issues is, therefore, not intended to be conclusive in any sense but simply to make the questions arise and to suggest terms in which the answers may be sought. I have tried to be as explicit as possible in explaining formal procedures, but I have not thought it necessary to provide exercises for developing facility in such procedures. Enough ways of creating such exercises have been suggested and enough proofs have been left undone that users of this book should find no lack of means for developing technical facility.

Chapters 1–8 represent a connected exposition of the propositional calculus. Chapter 8 may be omitted if metatheory is not to be discussed.

Chapter 6 is intended mainly to provide a contrast to the natural deduction techniques used in Chapter 7 and in the rest of the book. Chapters 1–5 carry the discussion of the propositional calculus through its development by means of truth tables and could be used alone if the theorems as opposed to the techniques of propositional logic are the main subject of interest.

The discussion of modalities in Chapter 9 presupposes Chapters 1–7, as does the discussion of quantification in Chapters 10 and 11.

Appendix A is a brief outline of traditional logic and its relation to modern logic; it therefore presupposes Chapters 10 and 11. Appendix B relates Polish notation to other notations in common use. Appendix C gathers together in one place the rules for the natural deduction formulations of the propositional calculus, the modal propositional calculus, and the predicate calculus.

Most of what I know about logic I learned from Professor Frederic B. Fitch of Yale University and Professor Alan Ross Anderson of the University of Pittsburgh. The rest I learned under the prodding of my students at Carleton College, whose interest and ability made me labor so mightily in teaching logic that writing this book became mainly a matter of organizing things which they had compelled me to think out.

I am grateful to Carleton College for granting me a leave of absence which enabled me to complete work on this book and for aiding financially in the duplication of an early version of the book for classroom use and in the preparation of the final manuscript. Professor Philip Jacklin of San Jose State College, Professor Donald S. Lee of Tulane University, Professor Grover Maxwell of the University of Minnesota, and a reader for Appleton-Century-Crofts provided many helpful comments on an early version of the book. Professor Justus Buchler and Mr. Jack K. Burton and Miss Vicki Cohen of Appleton-Century-Crofts were most helpful in the process of preparing the manuscript for publication. Deanna Dammer typed the final manuscript. Finally, I am grateful to my wife Andrea, who refused simply to type and made me, so far as she could, explain obscurities and write intelligible English sentences.

G.I.

CONTENTS

I am grateful to the colleagues who had comments and corrections on the first printing of this book, especially to Wade Mailette, Richard Davis, William Wisdom, Robert Sadowski, William Parry, Peter Geach, and P. C. Mason, all of whom pointed out errors which have been corrected in this printing.

G. I.

1

Inferability

1.1 We are constantly making assertions or claims to knowledge. Of course, this is not the case every time we speak. We may say "Ah!" when experiencing the pleasure of a cold shower on a hot day; we may say "I enjoyed that" after a concert; we may say "Go away" to an insistent door-to-door salesman; we may ask "What time is it?" when a train is late; in none of these cases is there any obvious or immediate claim to know anything. We may say "That was a good concert," "This is a fine piece of material," "He is a good man," "You really ought not to do that"; whether such remarks as these would normally constitute claims to knowledge is a matter of great dispute among philosophers, but a matter which need not be discussed here.[1]

Fortunately there are clearer cases: "It's raining"; "Two and two makes four"; "Physical space is curved"; "La plume de ma tante est sur la table de mon oncle"; "All men are mortal"; "Babe Ruth hit sixty home runs in 1927"; "The sedge has withered from the lake." People making utterances of these sorts would normally be thought to be claiming to know something, to be asserting something. This would not always be true, even here, of course. Someone might be merely considering a possibility, practicing his French accent, or reading a poem. But these **sentences** are clearly of sorts designed primarily for knowledge-claiming jobs, and it would not be difficult to tell in fact whether a knowledge-claim was being made. We could simply

---

[1] For a selection of readings dealing with this and related issues, see Taylor [47]. (Numbers in brackets in this and following footnotes refer to appropriately numbered items in the Bibliography on pp. 177–179.)

ask the person making the utterance *how* he knew, that is, we could ask him to **support** his assertion; and in case no such claim was in question, this request would be rejected as beside the point: "I *don't* know yet" or "Don't be silly; I'm just reciting a poem." Whenever a knowledge-claim *is* being made, however, the question "How do you know?" seems very much in order; in fact, the question's being in order seems to be a fair indicator of such a claim's being made.

1.2   There are various ways in which the question "How do you know?" can be answered: "How do you know it's raining?" "I can just see that it is"; or "There's a drumming sound on the roof"; or "Somebody told me." There are any number of ways in which one might support a knowledge-claim made in uttering any one of the sentences we have considered. One way of responding to the question "How do you know?", namely "I just do," is often a way of saying that the knowledge-claim in question does not *require* to be supported but is known "intuitively" or "directly."[2] When such a claim is justified, if ever, is another important and much discussed question but, again, one we need not face.

What is important for our purposes is that in innumerable cases knowledge-claims *do* require support and that one characteristic way (not the only way) of offering such support is by making *another* claim from which the original claim is supposedly **inferable**. It is this inferability in virtue of which we can **argue** to one assertion from another which is the logician's concern.[3]

1.3   Having introduced the idea of inferability by referring to the kind of situation in which we seek to support a knowledge-claim, we must be careful at the outset to realize that questions about inferability arise in other situations as well. For instance, we may be aware of an inferability relationship and, upon learning that the assertion from which we may infer is true, thereby *come to know* "indirectly" what is inferable from it, as opposed to finding support for something

[2] See Peirce [31], 5.213–5.263, for this use of "intuitive." Whether anything is known intuitively in this sense is a matter of long-standing philosophical dispute. Russell [40], Ch. 5, represents one version of the search for something known in this way, whereas Peirce argues that nothing is thus known.

[3] The reflective reader may see why philosophers have sought the "directly known." If knowledge-claims are supported by other knowledge-claims, what supports the supporter? Must we either find a kind of knowledge which supports but does not need to be supported, or else be sceptics? Austin [4] and Peirce [31], 5.358–5.410, attempt to find ways between the horns of this dilemma.

we had already asserted. More important, we must realize that the question of inferability is separable from the question whether we want to make any of the assertions which are said to stand in this relationship. It is clearly possible to decide whether assertions are so related that one *could* infer one assertion from others without even considering their assertibility independently. We would want to say, for example, that the assertion that Julius Caesar was President of the United States was inferable from the assertions that Caesar had two heads and that everyone with two heads had been President of the United States, quite apart from the manifest falsity of all these assertions.

Once we are convinced that the question of whether one assertion is inferable from others is independent of the question whether any of them is worth asserting, occasions when we wish in fact to separate those questions are not hard to find. One way to *test* an assertion is to see what is inferable from it. If what is inferable turns out to be false, so much the worse for the assertion being tested. This kind of procedure, which is common in the testing of scientific hypotheses, would be impossible unless we could first determine what inferability relationships hold and then go on to the question of the status of the assertions claimed to stand in this relation. Again, we may have acquired a number of bits of information which we later see to be related in such a way that some of them are inferable from others. To discover such a relationship is to understand better something which we already in some sense knew. In these important cases, for which those familiar with the sciences will readily be able to provide examples but which can equally well be illustrated from common life and discourse, it is essential that we be able to consider independently the question whether an assertion is inferable from others and the question whether we wish to *make* any of the assertions.

1.4 Inferability, then, is our subject. A word is in order about just what we may and what we may not hope to learn. The premise of all that follows is that the reader is already reasonably skilled at recognizing relationships of inferability, that he can usually tell when one assertion can or cannot be inferred from another, or is or is not supported by another.[4] What we are to discuss is what makes such relationships hold, "theoretical logic," if you will, rather than "practical logic."

[4] The reader who is more interested in practice in recognizing relationships of inferability may consult Beardsley [5].

Now it is unlikely that knowing how to recognize inferability relationships can be separated sharply from knowing what makes such relationships hold. On the one hand, the unlettered "man of good judgment" might be said to know the principles of inferability "implicitly," to the point that one wonders whether learning the Latin names of various "fallacies" represents any advance in wisdom. Conversely, one is unlikely to emerge from a study of "theoretical logic" without being a *little* better at recognizing inferability relationships. Theoretical logic, moreover, has its own techniques, so that some kind of "practice" is required even here. For some, these techniques will be easy; for others, difficult. For some, they will be interesting; for others, dull. It is important in any case to understand them if any of the other issues we shall be discussing are to be clear.

Besides questions about how theoretical logic relates to the actual ability to make inferences, one can ask about logic's place among other modes of human knowledge and experience. This is a philosophical question and, although we cannot hope to deal with it here, the fact that there are such questions should make anyone who claims to be a philosopher want to know something about logic.

2

Propositions

2.1 It is often interesting to ask of a certain quality not just what things in fact have it but what sort of things might *conceivably* have it; clarity about an issue of this sort can forestall all kinds of perplexities. It is in fact false that the desk I am seated at is red (it is some other color), but it seems more than just false that the sound of a truck laboring up a grade is red. (Metaphors aside, it is just not the sort of thing which is colored at all, and that is not because it only comes in black or white.) This sort of reflection[1] can cause difficulty for the philosopher when a question of the form "What sort of thing has such-and-such a quality?" is asked and none of the sorts of things which lie "ready-to-hand" as candidates for the role of bearer of the quality in question seems completely comfortable in that role. For it is in just such circumstances that, if we are convinced that *something* has this quality, we begin to "postulate" things precisely to fill that role, things which, in the nature of the case, are not "familiar" to the ordinary man in the way that desks and pencils and clouds are.

2.2 To bring these rather abstract musings to bear on present issues — of what sort of things can it be said that they are or are not inferable from one another? I have spoken of assertions, utterances, knowledge-claims. Can these be identified with "familiar" kinds of entities (where, by "familiar" is meant something like "not conjured up for the specific purpose of solving this philosophical perplexity")? What possibilities for such identifications are there? If they fail, what

---

[1] See Ryle [44], pp. 16ff., for a discussion of the notion of "category" which is essentially what is involved here.

kinds of "postulations" must we make? I do not propose to discuss these questions in detail, only to indicate how logic can give rise to such philosophical questions.

Two candidates for the role of things which are inferable from one another, **facts** and **sentences**, seem to lie ready-to-hand in the sense that everybody in some sense knows what facts and sentences are and no particular perplexities seem to surround these notions *themselves* such that, if we invoked them, someone could reproach us for attempting to explain the well-understood in terms of the less well-understood. (It may not be obvious that facts and sentences are ready-to-hand in this sense, but let us assume for now that they are.[2])

Although we may commonly speak of some fact being inferable from something or other, facts seem not to have been considered seriously very often for this role.[3] One reason, I suppose, is a conviction, sometimes unexamined, in other cases part of an elaborate theory of mind and knowledge, that is it not so much in the world that the relation of inferability obtains as it is in our thought and discourse about the world.[4] Certainly the terminology so far used — "assertions," "utterances," and so on — seems to suggest such a view. Another reason is that in many clear cases of inferability, such as the example in 1.3, it is difficult to see that any "facts" are involved at all.

What of sentences? Here we must first make a distinction between a sentence considered as a repeatable linguistic entity, a **type**, and a sentence considered as a single occurrence of such an entity, a **token**.[5] In the first sense, you can repeat a sentence I utter; you can produce the same sentence-type. In the second sense, you cannot; each utterance is a separate token. In either sense, sentences seem to qualify as elements in our "thought and discourse about the world." But, for many reasons, sentences in either sense seem to fail to fulfill the requirements which the entities which enter into the relationship of inferability must meet if that relationship is to have the properties only a little reflection can show it must have.

[2] For doubts about the concept "fact," for example, see Strawson in Pitcher [33], pp. 37ff.

[3] But see Mitchell [27], pp. 109ff.

[4] For a modern expression of the view, ultimately due to Aristotle and widely held among medieval philosophers, which sharply distinguishes between the "logical" and "real" orders, see Veatch [48].

[5] The terminology is due to Peirce. See, for example, [31], 4.537.

Sentence-tokens can, I think, be dismissed out of hand. To regard sentence-tokens as the entities which enter into inferability relationships would be to regard questions about inferability as arising anew for each utterance of a given set of sentence-tokens. Taking the example mentioned in 1.3 and using quotation marks to make it clear that sentences in *some* sense are being considered for the role of entities inferable from one another, the hypothesis that sentence-tokens fulfill this role amounts to the hypothesis that the claim that "Julius Caesar was President of the United States" is inferable from "Everyone with two heads has been President of the United States" and "Julius Caesar had two heads" must be considered anew for each occurrence of these sentences. But surely we know enough about inferability, even before we start to give a detailed account of it, to see that this would be absurd. Whatever may be true of inferability, it is at least clear that once the question "Does the inferability relationship mentioned in 1.3 hold?" is answered, it is answered for all.

If we consider the claims of sentence-types to be the entities which enter into inferability relationships, we can perhaps avoid this difficulty, but there will be others. First of all, there are many sentence-types which do not seem appropriate for making knowledge-claims, as we saw right at the outset, and it has been argued that inferability relationships primarily hold among such claims, or at least among sentences usable to make such claims.[6] Let us limit ourselves to such sentences, to what the grammarians might call **declarative** sentences. But now it becomes clear that sentence-types *as such* are not appropriate to the role for which we are considering them. The way to see this is to look a little more closely at what we must say about those entities which enter into the relationship of inferability and then see why we cannot say these things about sentence-types.

2.3 Consider our example again. "Everyone with two heads has been President of the United States." Consider now a slight variation. Let us, for example, change this sentence-type to "Everybody with two heads has been President of the United States." Now this change is clearly sufficient to make this a different sentence-type from the original, for the first word-types are different. But is this "trivial" change,

---

[6] Much interesting work has been done, however, in the study of logical relations among things which are not knowledge-claims. See, for example, Rescher [39] and Harrah [18].

as we might say, sufficient to affect the question of inferability? Surely not, we are tempted to say. Whatever enters into such a relationship is invariant under such a change. It is not the sentence-type but rather what someone could assert in uttering it.

It is not difficult to arrive at the same conclusion in other instances, for example, where we have not merely verbal variations but what have been called **emotive** variations as well. One assertion might be inferable from another and be phrased in such a way as to express either favor or distaste without affecting the inferability relationships into which it enters. If I say "She is skinny," you may infer from my saying so that I am not attracted to her, something you could not infer from my saying "She is svelte." In either case, however, my *assertion* is likely to be the same, and what can be inferred about her from it (not what can be inferred about me from my making it) is, consequently, likely to be the same. Or consider the same assertion made in different languages. I do not wish to argue that there is any simple and straightforward way of telling when two sentences are being used to make one assertion, or that emotive force, the *way* an assertion is made, is unimportant, or that it is easy to say when sentences in different languages can be used to make the same assertion. The only point for the moment is that the logical relation of inferability is invariant with respect to many such grammatical, emotive, and linguistic variations which make for different sentence-types; it is, therefore, not sentence-types which stand to one another in this relation.

Consider the converse question: are there cases where variations in inferability are not matched by corresponding variations in sentence-types? When a sentence-type is ambiguous, it may be used to make now one assertion, now another, one of which may be inferable from a given set of other assertions, one not.[7] In cases of this kind, we will no doubt resolve the ambiguity with the help of the context in favor of the assertion which *is* inferable, but this in itself is sufficient to show that it is not *merely* sentence-types which are at issue. In such cases, where a single sentence-type may be used to make different assertions depending upon the resolution of ambiguities, variations in infer-

---

[7] This is also true of sentence-types which we should hesitate to regard as ambiguous but which do contain words whose reference varies with the circumstances of utterance, words like "this," "I," "now," "yesterday," "here," and so on. For discussion of some problems raised by such words, see Quine [38], p. 101, and the works referred to in the footnote to that page.

ability need not be matched by corresponding variations in sentence-types; therefore, it is not sentence-types which stand to one another in that relation.

2.4 What does, then? Many terms have been used: "judgments," "thoughts," "statements," "meanings," "propositions." These terms are far from equivalent and each raises its own problems, but they do share the characteristic of *not* being among the ready-to-hand entities so far considered. That is to say, they are all notions which are in varying degrees puzzling on their own account (or so they have seemed to philosophers, both those who would dispense with them for that very reason,[8] and those who have nonetheless felt constrained to appeal to them.[9]) I do not propose to decide among them here, only to try to suggest why this issue has arisen and to record my suspicion that somewhere in this area the answer must lie, that there is no way to avoid the puzzles which go with the realization that the logical relation of inferability does not obtain between such relatively unproblematic sorts of entities as facts or sentences.[10] As for the term "assertion" which has appeared hitherto, it seems unsuited in that it tends to obscure precisely the distinction, made in 1.3, between a relation of inferability holding and the entities thus related being "asserted." Unasserted assertions, in whose inferability relationships we are often interested, seem to be needlessly paradoxical. Without staking anything on the term other than that it refers neither to facts nor to sentences, I propose for the remainder of this discussion to call those entities which enter into the logical relation of inferability **propositions.**

[8] See the articles by Pitcher and Woozley in Iseminger [21].
[9] See the article by Frege in Iseminger [21].
[10] The currently fashionable term "statement" does not seem to me to avoid all these puzzles by any means. For its use, see Strawson [45], pp. 3–4, 9–12. For objections to it, see Mitchell [27], pp. 105ff.

3

Logical truth

3.1 Another way to characterize propositions is to say that they are things of the sort which can be true or false. (It would be possible to argue even more convincingly that things of the sort which can be true or false can be neither facts nor sentences than we were able to argue that the things which stand to one another in the logical relation of inferability can be neither facts nor sentences. The argument would be parallel to that by which we ruled out facts and sentences in 2.2 and 2.3.) That the things which stand in the inferability relationship to one another are the same as the things that are true or false should not surprise us when we recall that the notion of inferability arose in the first instance in connection with the ideas of supporting or discovering some *truth* by virtue of its relation to others.

The notion of truth has challenged philosophical reflection for centuries; we cannot hope to clarify it very much here, only to use it. We may say that a proposition is true if and only if it is worthy of belief, but I shall not stop to explore this account, since I am not mainly concerned with the concept of truth in general.[1] I want to begin by establishing at least an apparent difference between the proposition which would normally be expressed by the sentence "Brutus killed Caesar" and the proposition which would be normally expressed by the sentence "Either Brutus killed Caesar or it's not the case that Brutus killed Caesar." (The clumsy circumlocution "proposition which would normally be expressed by the sentence," which, the reader

---

[1] For discussion of some of the problems surrounding the concept of truth, see the articles in Pitcher [33].

11

should be convinced by the discussion just concluded, is necessary in strictness, will be dispensed with henceforth in favor of "proposition.") One way of seeing the difference between the propositions, both of which seem to be true, is to observe that when I know the latter I know nothing about history, despite its apparently being about a historical event.[2] We would be (properly) annoyed by a history book which included only propositions like it. Since propositions of the first sort are true according to, in this case, the historical facts of the matter, they are often called **factual truths**.

A random sampling of true propositions would no doubt disclose that a vast majority of those which immediately occur to us are of this sort, to the point where one might wonder whether there really are any of the others, or at least what the point of asserting them might be. This suspicion is reinforced by the knowledge that propositions of this sort have often been called **tautologies**,[3] a term which has a perfectly normal use in which it implies, among other things, that a proposition so labeled is trivial and hardly worth asserting. I want to defer this issue, for its answer will lead us to the heart of the questions we shall discuss, and turn now to an attempt to characterize a little more fully this latter class of propositions,[4] henceforth to be called **logical truths**.

3.2   So far, what we have said of these truths is negative, that they are *not* true in virtue of the facts they apparently "refer to." How would we respond if someone asked us what *did* make it true that either Brutus killed Caesar or it's not the case that Brutus killed Caesar? (*That* it is true let us accept; people have had their doubts.)[5] One way to reply would be something like this: "Well, you see, when you say 'either . . . or' you mean that one or the other proposition thus joined is true, and, if these two propositions are a proposition and its denial, one of them *has* to be true, so any 'either . . . or' of this sort would be true, whether it was ostensibly about Roman history, men on Mars,

---

[2] See Wittgenstein [50], 4.461.

[3] See Wittgenstein [50], 4.46ff.

[4] Whether the distinction between these two classes of propositions ultimately stands up has been a matter of much recent controversy, stemming from Quine [37], Ch. II. For a defense of the distinction against Quine's attack, see the article by Grice and Strawson in Ammerman [1].

[5] See, for example, the argument by Brouwer, from the viewpoint in the philosophy of mathematics known as "intuitionism," in Benacerraf and Putnam [6], pp. 78–84. For a defense of the principle attacked by Brouwer, see Russell [42], Ch. 20.

or the 1914 National League pennant race. It's a matter of the *meanings* of words like 'either,' 'or,' and 'not,' or, as we might say, the concepts of disjunction and negation, and their interconnections." We might sum this up by saying that logically true propositions are true in virtue of the meanings of words, or in virtue of conceptual connections.[6]

This is not to say that they are truths *about* the meanings of words, as is a proposition such as " 'Red' has the same meaning as 'rouge.' " For such truths are just special kinds of factual truths, dependent upon the way languages happen to have developed. I leave the reader to convince himself that this is not the case with propositions like "Either Brutus killed Caesar or it's not the case that Brutus killed Caesar." (Remember, propositions, *not* sentences.) Whether we should go on to say that it is some kind of timeless fact in a logical heaven which makes such propositions true, I shall not discuss.[7]

There are also **factual falsehoods**, of which "Caesar killed Brutus" is an example, and **logical falsehoods**, of which "Brutus killed Caesar and it's not the case that Brutus killed Caesar" is an example. We may regard propositions as being divided first into truths and falsehoods, those worthy of belief and those not worthy of belief; we may then say that the truths are divided into factual and logical truths and the falsehoods into factual and logical falsehoods. A proposition will fall under one and only one of these four classifications. In what follows we shall not often concern ourselves with the two kinds of falsehoods.

3.3   There is a slightly more technical way of saying what makes logical truths true, a way which will prove useful as we proceed. This is to say that logical truths are **true in virtue of their form**. In order to understand such a remark, of course, we shall have to find out what is meant by speaking of the "form" of a proposition, and this is our next task.

Clarification by contrast is often useful, and here, I suppose, the most natural contrast with "form" is "content." Without pretending to clarify *this* notion, we can say that the **content** of the proposition "Brutus killed Caesar" is something about Roman history, and so,

[6] This is not a universally accepted account of the nature of logical truth. See Nagel in Feigl and Sellars [13], pp. 191–210, for a sketch of some other views. It is to be emphasized that the account I have sketched is not yet the view known as "linguistic conventionalism." For an example of this view, see Hahn in Iseminger [21]. For criticisms, see Pap in Iseminger [21].

[7] See Russell in Iseminger [21] for an argument tending in this direction.

apparently, would be the content of the proposition "Either Brutus killed Caesar or it's not the case that Brutus killed Caesar." On the natural supposition that the form is what is left over after the content is removed, we can discover the form of the proposition "Either Brutus killed Caesar or it's not the case that Brutus killed Caesar" by removing all references to Roman history. With a **complex proposition**, that is to say, a proposition whose components include other propositions, the most natural way to do this is by simply eliminating these **component propositions**. (We defer any account of the form of the **simple proposition** "Brutus killed Caesar.") If we replace the proposition "Brutus killed Caesar" by "***" wherever it occurs (and, if there were other component propositions, each of them by some other stand-in), the result is the schema "Either *** or it's not the case that ***." We will say of any such schema, then, that it represents a form of a given proposition if and only if reinserting the content, in this case the proposition "Brutus killed Caesar," wherever it has been expunged results in the original proposition. Two propositions will be of the *same* form if there is some single schema from which each of them results if the appropriate content is reinserted in it.

We can now translate our earlier remarks concerning logical truth as follows: to say that the proposition "Either Brutus killed Caesar or it's not the case that Brutus killed Caesar" is true in virtue of its form is simply to say that *any* proposition of that *same* form (for example, "Either it's snowing or it's not the case that it's snowing" or "Either Johnson is President or it's not the case that Johnson is President") is true and for the same reasons. And in order to see this, it is necessary only to reflect on the meanings of "either," "or," and "not," as we did above. Finally, to nail down the contrast between "Either Brutus killed Caesar or it's not the case that Brutus killed Caesar" and "Brutus killed Caesar," it should be sufficient to reflect that, even given some account of the form of the latter proposition (for example, "A killed B," where the "A" and "B" stand for names here, not, as before, where "***" stood for a whole proposition), we cannot say that *any* proposition of that form is true, for it would not be difficult to think of counter-examples.

A word of caution concerning the notion of logical form is necessary. It might be asked why "Either Brutus killed Caesar or it's not the case that Brutus killed Caesar" could not have been taken to have the form "Either *** or $$$." Replacing "***" with "Brutus killed

Caesar" and "$$$" with "It's not the case that Brutus killed Caesar," we get the original proposition. (Obviously it could not be taken to have the form "Either *** or ***." Why not?) The answer is that it *could*. There is not just *one* form, necessarily, which a given proposition can be shown to have. And the form which we consider will affect our results. It is certainly *not* true that *any* proposition of the form "Either *** or $$$" is true; counter-examples are not hard to find. (Think of some.)

It evidently follows immediately that a proposition is not shown *not* to be logically true simply by being shown to be of some form such that not *all* propositions of that form are true. If this were the case, we would have shown that our example both was and was not a logical truth, an embarrassing result, to say the least. The discovery of the form which is the one we want to consider is not a task for which handy rules can be given. It is one of the eventual aims of logic (not to be pursued very far here) to give a kind of inventory of the forms propositions may have,[8] so that it at least becomes clear what the possibilities are. It may be some consolation to reflect that showing that there is *a* form which a proposition may be shown to have such that all propositions of that form are true is *sufficient* to show that the proposition in question *is* logically true, no matter what other analyses into other forms may reveal. If this were not the case, finding out whether a proposition were logically true would be more than a tedious task; it would be impossible.

3.4 A form, then, is discovered by breaking a proposition up into components, either other propositions or smaller units, **concepts**, and replacing some of these components with blanks. And the logical truth of a logically true proposition will depend upon the concepts which are left after we have replaced some components of the original proposition with blanks in order to reveal its form. One way of looking at the job of the logician is to say that it consists of showing relationships among logical truths and developing means for testing them. How this description of the logician's job connects with the task of giving an account of inferability will become clear shortly; considering only the present description, we may expect that the logician's job

---

[8] Quine [38], Ch. 5, which should not be attempted until the fundamentals of logic have been grasped at least to the extent that they are presented in this book, may be read as an attempt to reduce to manageable dimensions the apparent variety of propositional forms.

would then boil down to the examination of the concepts which are left in the representation of forms. This is true, but we must be careful here.

If we take as our criterion of logical truth "true in virtue of conceptual connections," and see the logician as studying those concepts which are left over after "content" has been extruded in search of "form," it should be immediately apparent that there is no predetermined set of concepts which, as it were, simply *present* themselves to the logician as objects of his study.

Consider a proposition like "Every bachelor is unmarried." This seems to be a logical truth, as opposed to a factual truth, but it's perfectly clear that any account of its logical truth would have to include a discussion of the relations between the concepts "bachelor" and "unmarried," as well as "every" and "is." The notion of bachelorhood may thus appear to be a suitable subject for the logician, and, depending upon one's interest in a concept, one *may* study its "logic" by seeing how it enters into logical truths.[9] In practice, however, the logician, constrained by his aim of investigating what is inferable from what, considers concepts which are most frequently relevant to the inferability relationship, and it seems, on the face of it, that *more* inferability relationships are going to depend upon concepts such as those usually embodied in words like "and," "not," and "every" than on the concepts of bachelorhood and unmarriedness. The remainder of our study, therefore, will not concern itself with bachelorhood.

Even within the set of notions we shall study, there are important differences which make it convenient to proceed in a certain order. Roughly, the difference is between concepts which appear in propositions in such a way that when the appropriate form has been revealed the blanks would have to be filled by whole propositions in order to reconstruct the original proposition, and those which appear in propositions in such a way that when the appropriate form has been revealed the blanks would be filled merely by parts of propositions. An example

---

[9] For an example of a formal study of the "logic" of concepts other than those we shall study, see Hintikka [19]. This notion of studying the "logic" of a concept is more frequently associated with "informal" studies such as some of those in Malcolm [25]. For discussions of the contrast between "formal" and "informal" logic and the utility of formal logic in general, see the final two selections in Iseminger [21], by Strawson and Quine.

of a form involving concepts of the first sort would be "Either *** or it's not the case that ***"; an example of a form involving concepts of the second sort would be "Every % is $." (This latter form, of course, does not carry logical truth with it.) Thus one part of our study will concern notions like "or," "not," and so forth; another, notions like "every" and "some." Since the logic of the latter notions can be more readily understood if it is possible to appeal to the logic of the former, we shall study them in the order in which we mentioned them.

4

Entailment

4.1 We must now apply these remarks about propositions and logical truth to our question "What makes inferability relationships hold?"

The first thing to be noticed is that a relation of inferability seems to be readily expressible as a particular kind of proposition, namely an "if . . . then," or **conditional** proposition. When, for example, we were discussing whether the proposition "Julius Caesar was President of the United States" was inferable from the two propositions "Everyone with two heads has been President of the United States" and "Julius Caesar had two heads," we could equally well have stated our question as a question about the complex proposition "If everyone with two heads has been President of the United States and Julius Caesar had two heads, then Julius Caesar was President of the United States." And in general we could turn questions about inferability into questions about the relation between the **antecedent** (what comes after "if") and the **consequent** (what comes after "then") of a complex conditional proposition. "If . . . then" is often a signal that a claim is being made that something in some sense is inferable from something else. In fact, if we recall once again the reflection in 1.3, it may appear that the above way of stating our question clarifies it, for it seems to invite us to consider the inferability relationship which can be claimed by a conditional proposition (and which is to be our topic) independently of considering the truth or falsity of the separate propositions which are claimed to stand in that relation. (The example was chosen, in part, because it is an example of an inferability relationship which *does* hold, even though the propositions thus related are obviously false.)

19

4.2 If we have agreed to describe our task in this new way, as the examination of conditional propositions, it is tempting to say straight off that our job is to look for *true* conditional propositions. But conditional propositions, like propositions in general, can be factually true (or false) or logically true (or false). We must pause to consider what implications this distinction has for our task.

Consider a couple of examples: (i) "If this litmus paper is placed in acid, then it turns red" and (ii) "If either it's raining or it's snowing and it's not the case that it's raining, then it's snowing." Both of these seem to be true conditional propositions, and indeed in either case the assertion of the antecedent (which in (ii) is itself compounded of a number of propositions) would be taken as supplying some kind of good grounds for the assertion of the consequent. But the differences are equally clear; it seems obvious that the consequent in (i) does not strictly "follow from" the antecedent. One can imagine circumstances under which the antecedent could be true and the consequent false. This is not so with (ii). Given the (complex) antecedent, the consequent *must* be true. Correspondingly, a little reflection will show that (i) is a factual truth while (ii) is a logical truth. The truth of (i) depends on facts ascertained by chemists, while we need know nothing of the weather to know (ii). We can discover a form for (ii) such that any proposition of that form is true, while we cannot do this with (i). We shall restrict our attention to the strong relationship which holds between antecedent and consequent in (ii), the relationship in virtue of which the consequent can be **validly deduced** from the antecedent, or, alternatively, the relationship in virtue of which the antecedent **entails** the consequent.[1]

A word is in order, however, concerning propositions like (i). The move from antecedent to consequent of a conditional proposition like (i) is often called an **inductive** inference. To say that in such cases the consequent does not strictly follow from the antecedent, or that the antecedent does not entail the consequent, is not to say that such inferences are unjustified or incapable of being evaluated as better or worse than one another, or that the logician has nothing to say about them. It is certainly *not* the job of the logician in his study to ascertain

---

[1] The term "entails" in this technical sense, which will be used henceforth in this book to describe the relationship which is the central concern of logic, is due to Moore [28], p. 291.

such facts as would warrant the inference expressible by (i); it is rather the job of the chemist. There are, nevertheless, difficult questions concerning the general conditions under which we have a right to assert propositions such as (i). These are questions of **inductive logic** and not questions in chemistry. People have in fact argued that all inference is really inductive (so have people argued that all inference is really deductive).[2] The reader interested in pursuing questions of inductive logic will find nothing further to interest him here,[3] but this is only because we choose to restrict ourselves more or less arbitrarily to questions of entailment and hence of deductive validity.

4.3 In outlining our topic, then, we have come to conceive of our task as the study of entailments by means of the study of ways of testing and interrelating logically true conditional propositions and, in particular, by means of the study of notions such as "and," "every," and others in virtue of which such propositions most frequently *are* logically true. To this task we now turn, beginning with some concepts, "and," "or," "not," and, of course, "if . . . then," which form complex propositions when applied to other propositions. Having dealt with propositions which obviously involve these concepts, we shall also be able to see that many propositions which do not so obviously involve them can in fact be understood in terms of them.

[2] For the former view, see Mill [26], pp. 136ff; for the latter, see Russell in Copi and Gould [11], p. 214n. It must be stated, however, that Russell, as often happens, can be found on the other side of this issue in later years and in a somewhat different context. See [43], p. 119.

[3] A selection of writings dealing with issues in inductive logic can be found in Foster and Martin [15].

5

Truth-functions

5.1 We shall study logical truths by developing various **formal systems** which attempt to display all and only the logical truths in the area we are concerned with. These systems are called "formal" partly because, if they are successful, they enable us to change many of the questions about the propositions in question into easily answered questions about the form or shape of the formulas by which we represent them and partly because, in order for this aim to be realized, we proceed "formally," that is, doing only what fully explicit rules permit us to do, in constructing such systems. These systems are useful not merely in dealing with propositions of the sort we have called "true in virtue of their form," though the occurrence of the word "form" in both cases is potentially misleading. Euclidean geometry, for instance, is an example of a formal system in which the propositions represented by it are not true in virtue of their form but, if true at all, true in virtue of facts about space. If formal systems can be used to study propositions other than logical truths, they can also be studied in themselves, in abstraction from any questions about the propositions their formulas may represent. The mathematician's attitude towards geometry is of this kind, and so is that of many logicians towards formal systems of the sort we shall be considering.[1] With these qualifications in mind, we shall consider formal systems primarily for what they can help us learn about logical truths.

---

[1] Hilbert and Ackermann [20] is an example of a text representing this attitude towards formal systems.

Characterized as generally as possible, a formal system to be used in dealing with a certain set of concepts and propositions must consist of a set of symbols to represent the concepts in question,[2] rules stating permissible ways of combining these symbols into formulas representing propositions or propositional forms, some means of giving the basic properties of the concepts we are interested in to the symbols representing them, and, finally, a way of selecting from among the formulas the ones which represent propositions of the sort we are interested in. (In the case of geometry considered as a set of propositions about space, these propositions would be true propositions about space; in our case, they will be logical truths of different kinds.)

5.2 We have decided to turn first to logical truths whose truth depends on their being of forms consisting of (i) blanks to be filled by whole propositions and (ii) concepts like "if . . . then," "and," "not," and "or." Our first task, then, is to provide ourselves with symbols. Instead of blanks, which quickly become clumsy and unperspicuous, we shall use lower-case letters, beginning with "p" and proceeding in alphabetical order as far as necessary (seldom past "s") as stand-ins for the component propositions which in part make up the complex propositions we are studying. We call these letters **proposition stand-ins.** (It will be important, of course, when finding the form of a proposition made up of others to put the *same* stand-in for a given proposition throughout and a *different* stand-in for each different proposition.) For our representation of the concepts we are studying we shall use upper-case letters as follows:

> "A" for "or"
> "N" for "not" or "it's not the case that"
> "C" for "if . . . then"
> "K" for "and" [3]

[2] Hence the term "symbolic logic," which is often applied to the study to which this book is mainly devoted and, quite inappropriately, withheld from more "traditional" parts of logic, such as those discussed below in Appendix A. Lewis Carroll (C. L. Dodgson), mathematician and logician as well as renowned writer of fantasy, applied the term to a quite "traditional" enterprise in [8].

[3] The use of upper-case letters instead of special symbols such as those given in Appendix B below is one of the distinguishing features of the system of notation adopted here, due to Łukasiewicz and commonly known as "Polish notation." It may be helpful in remembering which upper-case letters are intended to represent which concepts to associate "N" with negation, "A" with alternation, "C" with the conditional, and "K" (since "C" is already used) with conjunction.

The upper-case letters are called **propositional connectives** because, in general, they represent concepts which *connect* propositions so as to form complex propositions. We may also apply this term to the concepts themselves. These symbols are not stand-ins for the concepts; they are formal representations of them (that is, they will be if our system is a successful one).

5.3 We have now a kind of vocabulary of symbols; we require next what might be called a grammar. It will consist of what are called **formation rules**, which will tell us what combinations of symbols make sense, or are "sentences." Bearing in mind what the symbols are to represent (or, as is often said, their **intended interpretation**), we should have no difficulty seeing what the general requirements are. Just as, for example, "and not or" makes no sense as it stands, so "KNA" will not be a "sentence" or, as is usually said, a **well-formed formula (wff)** in our system. In general it should be clear that we want our propositional connectives to enter into wff's only insofar as they relate to proposition stand-ins. For example, "N" will make a wff when attached to a single proposition stand-in; "A," "K," and "C" when attached to two proposition stand-ins. (Reflection on the intended interpretation of these symbols should make this clear.)

The *order* in which the connectives and stand-ins should be put together to form wff's is not so obvious. "Not" occurs in various places within propositions, but for our purposes it will be convenient to specify that it precede the proposition it is to qualify. (Thus "Np" will be a wff but "pN" will not.) Similarly "and," "or," and "if . . . then" clearly join *two* propositions, the first two usually being found between the propositions they join, the latter "surrounding" the first of the two propositions joined. Here again convenience dictates that in our notation we write the two proposition stand-ins which together with the propositional connective are to form the wff immediately following the connective. (Thus "Kpq," "Apq," and "Cpq" will be wff's, but "pCq," for example, will not.)[4]

Although the immediate results of reading some propositions thus expressed in the order suggested by our formation rules might not be intuitively appealing, the reader should be able to convince himself

---

[4] The ordering conventions adopted here, which make it unnecessary to use parentheses or any other kind of punctuation to make formulas unambiguous, are the other distinguishing feature of Polish notation. See Appendix B below and Kneale and Kneale [22], pp. 513–524.

that the ways in which these connective concepts join or apply to propositions in ordinary discourse can in fact be accurately represented in the way suggested.

We now have a general idea of the way we want to concatenate our symbols, but more is required. For one thing, we want to state our formation rules in a sufficiently general way to be able to tell by looking at some concatenation of symbols and applying our rules to it whether it is a wff; as matters stand we have said that "Apq" is a wff, but how about "Aqp"? Clearly we want it to be, but we must state our rules in such a way as to make it clear. Again, we want to be able to make more complicated wff's than those made with only two stand-ins and a connective. What about "AqCpr," for example? Our logic would certainly be impoverished if we could not use wff's with this kind of complication and deal with propositions whose forms they represent.

To achieve these aims we require two more technical notions, those of a **metavariable** and a **recursive definition**. A metavariable is a symbol which stands for any concatenation of the symbols already introduced. We shall use as metavariables the italicized lower-case letter "*p*," "*q*," etc. Thus, for example, when we see "*p*," we are to understand it as standing indifferently for "p," "q," "Apq," etc. In some cases, which will be clear from the context, the metavariables will stand for wff's only. Thus, for example, "K*pq*" will often mean "any formula made up of 'K' followed by two wff's."

A recursive definition is a procedure whereby we specify what things are to be covered by a term by first enumerating an initial stock of such things, then saying how to make more of them out of this initial stock, and finally saying that there are no others.

Employing these notions we may now give formation rules for our propositional variables and logical constants as follows:

(i) A proposition stand-in is a wff.
(ii) If *p* is a wff, then N*p* is a wff.
(iii) If *p* and *q* are wff's, then A*pq*, K*pq*, and C*pq* are wff's.
(iv) There are no wff's besides those specified in (i), (ii), and (iii).

The reader should convince himself that the forms of all and only those expressions made up of component propositions and "not," "or," "and," and "if . . . then," which *do* make sense, no matter how complicated they may be, are in fact expressible as wff's according to these rules. (It's also worthwhile to reflect on the necessity of (iv), called the **extremal clause**.)

5.4 We must next specify how our connectives, "A," "C," "N," and "K," are to be understood if we are to be able to use them in telling when propositions depending upon the concepts they represent are logically true. One way of doing this is to exhibit how propositions of the sort which our formation rules so far permit us to represent vary in their truth or falsity according to the truth or falsity of the propositions of which they are made up. Thus, if we were to show how propositions of the form Kpq were true or false according to the truth or falsity of p and q themselves, we would have given a **definition** (in one sense of that term) of the constant "K." A way of summarizing this definition is to give a **truth table**, that is, a listing of the possible combinations of truth or falsity of two propositions joined by the "K," together with the associated **truth-value** (truth or falsity) of the resulting combination.[5] We may begin as follows, adopting obvious representations of "true" and "false." Although we shall ultimately employ our tables primarily in the study of logical truth, "t" and "f" here are to be thought of as representing the properties of worthiness of belief, shared by factual and logical truths, and unworthiness of belief, shared by factual and logical falsehoods, respectively.

$$K\,p\,q$$
$$t\ t$$
$$t\ f$$
$$f\ t$$
$$f\ f$$

Here we clearly have all the possible combinations of truth or falsity of two propositions represented (why?); we must now ask what to fill in under the "K," what value the whole combination takes for a given arrangement of truth-values of p and q. To do this we have only to reflect on our "intuitive"[6] concept of conjunction (which "K" is to

---

[5] Truth tables appear as early as Peirce [31], 3.387. Their invention is often attributed to Wittgenstein. See [50], 5.101.

[6] Here and throughout the rest of this book when "intuitive" views of certain concepts are appealed to, what is meant is something like "pre-analytic" or "unsophisticated." The sense of "intuition" discussed in note 2 to Ch. 1, which might seem to involve questions about some special faculty of direct and unchallengeable knowledge, is not at issue. See Quine [38], p. 36n.

represent) and the following truth table seems obviously to emerge as the required definition of "K": (Note that we use metavariables in giving definitions. Why?)

$$
\begin{array}{ccc}
\mathrm{K} & p & q \\
\mathrm{t} & \mathrm{t} & \mathrm{t} \\
\mathrm{f} & \mathrm{t} & \mathrm{f} \\
\mathrm{f} & \mathrm{f} & \mathrm{t} \\
\mathrm{f} & \mathrm{f} & \mathrm{f}
\end{array}
$$

Before we proceed to give similar definitions of our other connectives, a couple of extremely important points need to be made. First, a little reflection will show that this whole procedure presupposes that one can determine the truth or falsity of propositions formed by joining other propositions with "and" simply by referring to the truth or falsity of those component propositions. Another way of saying the same thing is to say that "and" is a **truth-functional** connective because the truth or falsity of a proposition formed by joining other propositions with it is a **function**, in the mathematical sense, of the truth or falsity of these latter, component propositions.

A related point is this: it is possible to proceed to discuss the techniques of truth-functional logic and the properties of "K," "A," and so on without even asking whether the associated concepts employed in ordinary discourse are truth-functional. In fact, as was suggested above, many of the questions logicians raise are answerable entirely independently of the intended interpretation of the symbols we have adopted. Given our stated aims, however, we could hardly defer this question forever. The temptation to do so often arises from the conviction that the answer will be the wrong one, that the connectives used in ordinary discourse are not truth-functional.

With these words of warning, then, we give the defining truth tables for our other connectives.

N p		A p q		C p q	
f	t	t t t		t t t	
t	f	t t f		f t f	
		t f t		t f t	
		f f f		t f f	

5.5 Let us consider briefly the issues which arise when we ask about the relation of our truth-functional notions to the concepts they are to represent.

It is relatively easy, I think, to show that *under the assumption that the concepts in question are truth-functional* our truth tables accurately display their "logical powers." To see this, one need only consider proposed alternative truth tables and see where they lead to undesirable results. With respect to the "C," for example, one might be tempted to make the last row take the value "f" under the "C." In support one could cite apparent instances of false conditional propositions with false antecedents and false consequents, for example, (i) "If the moon is made of green cheese, the Mediterranean is larger than the Pacific." Counter-examples, however, are equally easy to come by. Any conditional proposition expressing an entailment between false propositions will do. Let us, for illustration, take the one used previously: (ii) "If everyone with two heads has been President of the United States and Julius Caesar had two heads, then Julius Caesar was President of the United States." Under our assumption of truth-functionality, however, we must decide either that both (i) and (ii) are true or that they are both false. To decide that they are both *false* would mean that we would be unable to deal adequately with (ii) which, we have decided, expresses an entailment and which must, therefore, be not only true but logically true. To decide that they are both *true* leaves open the possibility of dealing with that entailment (which we have still to do, of course, when we can show that it is logically true), while it does not commit us to any view that the antecedent of (i) entails its consequent (a view which we should surely want to avoid) since to say that it is true is not to say that it is logically true. We may summarize this by saying that there is good reason to deny that all conditionals with false antecedents and false consequents are false; under the assumption of the truth-functionality of "if . . . then," this amounts to saying that there is good reason to assert that all such conditionals are true. Similar reflections should commend the table proposed as against any other possible table as well.

With regard to the table for "A," supposed to represent "or," a question may arise about the first row. Here we cannot claim that any other table would lead immediately to undesirable consequences, for there is a quite ordinary sense of "or" in whose representation the first row would be different. Any difficulties that may be felt here can be resolved simply by saying that there is an inclusive and an exclusive sense of "or" (a distinction which many languages, but not English, reflect), and we have chosen, for reasons which will become clear later, to represent the inclusive sense, the notion lawyers express by the locution "and/or." It would be possible to introduce a different connective with the truth table changed in the first row; it will also be possible to deal with the inclusive "or" in terms of the notions already present.

The overriding issue, however, is the assumption of truth-functionality. Are we justified, for our purposes, in regarding the concepts we are dealing with as truth-functional? We can discuss this issue more profitably after we have seen what consequences this assumption has for our account of entailment, which, after all, is our primary concern. The ease with which (as will become apparent) it is possible to manipulate truth-functional connectives may provide us with reason to hope that the concepts we are discussing may be represented in this way, although it is certainly not a reason for asserting this. For now we will proceed, coming as close as we can to representing those concepts truth-functionally and seeing what the consequences are.

5.6 Since we have given the definitions of our connectives in terms of metavariables, we have provided for the calculation of the truth-value of any wff provided for in our formation rules, no matter how complex. In order to do so we need only (i) make sure that we have covered all the possible combinations of "t's" and "f's" under the component proposition stand-ins, (ii) calculate according to the defining truth tables the values of the wff's which result from the immediate combinations of the proposition stand-ins with connectives, and (iii), taking these values, calculate the resulting values for the wff's which result from the further combination of these wff's with connectives, and so on, until we fill the column of truth-values under the upper-case letter which begins the wff (the **main connective**). A given letter, "t" or "f," under the main connective of a wff represents the truth-value which an expression of that form assumes when the truth-values of the propositions going to make it up are those assigned to the proposition stand-ins in that particular row of the truth table.

As for being sure that we have covered all the possible combinations of "t's" and "f's" of the proposition stand-ins in a given wff, it is easy to see that, in general, for a wff containing n different proposition stand-ins there will be 2^n such possible combinations (why?), and, therefore, 2^n rows in its truth table. One way to be sure that we have all the right rows is to begin with the proposition stand-in first in alphabetical order and write under each of its occurrences a column of $2^n/2$ "t's," filling out the column of 2^n letters with $2^n/2$ "f's." Then move to the next stand-in in alphabetical order, filling in its column by writing down, first, half as many "t's" as were put down successively in the preceding column, then half as many "f's," and so on down the column. If the procedure is continued in this fashion, cutting the successive "t's" and "f's" in half for each succeeding stand-in, the column under the last stand-in will be filled in with alternating "t's" and "f's." (Reflect on why this procedure achieves its stated purpose.) The order in which these columns are written down is a matter of convention, but there is a point in having some convention. If we do this, it is possible to identify a given connective simply by reading off the column of truth-values under it in its defining truth table. Thus "K" may be identified as (t, f, f, f).[7] This would not be possible without a convention such as we have adopted.

We now apply these remarks by calculating step by step the value of a wff, "KCprAqNp." Since there are three different proposition stand-ins, there will be eight rows to the truth table. We begin by assigning "t's" and "f's" to these stand-ins as described above, remembering to assign the same value to a given variable wherever it occurs in a given row. (Why?)

K	C	p	r	A	q	N	p
		t	t		t		t
		t	f		t		t
		t	t		f		t
		t	f		f		t
		f	t		t		f
		f	f		t		f
		f	t		f		f
		f	f		f		f

(handwritten in margin: p ⊃ R C q v p)

Referring for instructions to the definitions given of the connectives, we can first fill in under those which immediately join proposition stand-ins, in this case "N" and "C," thus:

K	C	p	r	A	q	N	p
	t	t	t		t	f	t
	f	t	f		t	f	t
	t	t	t		f	f	t
	f	t	f		f	f	t
	t	f	t		t	t	f
	t	f	f		t	t	f
	t	f	t		f	t	f
	t	f	f		f	t	f

[7] See Wittgenstein [50], 5.101.

Next, referring to the defining truth table of "A" and the columns
under "q" and under "N" (why?), we can calculate the column under
"A":

```
K C p r A q N p
  t t t t t f t
  f t f t t f t
  t t t f f f t
  f t f f f f t
  t f t t t t f
  t f f t t t f
  t f t t f t f
  t f f t f t f
```

Finally, referring to the defining truth table of "K" and the columns
under "C" and "A," we can complete the table:

```
K C p r A q N p
t t t t t t f t
f f t f t t f t
f t t t f f f t
f f t f f f f t
t t f t t t t f
t t f f t t t f
t t f t t f t f
t t f f t f t f
```

Now notice that the results of calculating the values of some wff's,
of which one of the simplest is "ApNp" (the reader will recognize this
as representing the form of one of our early examples, "Either Brutus
killed Caesar or it's not the case that Brutus killed Caesar") is a solid
column of "t's" under the main connective.

```
A p N p
t t f t
t f t f
```

What is the significance of this result? It is not hard to discover. A wff of
this sort, called a **truth table tautology** (**ttt**), clearly represents a
form such that a proposition of that form is true no matter what the
truth-values of its component propositions are; given our assumption
of truth-functionality, however, this means that propositions of this

form are true irrespective of variation in the only thing which could affect their truth. In other words, *any* proposition of this form is true. But this is how we have characterized logical truths, and they are just what we are looking for. Our task now reduces to discovering ttt's, in particular, given our concern with conditional propositions and, through them, valid deductive inferences, ttt's in which "C" is the main constant. This is a matter of simple mechanical calculation.

We now have the final item our formal system requires, a way of selecting from among the wff's the ones which represent forms we are interested in, that is to say, the **theorems**. In the present system a wff will be a theorem if and only if it is a ttt. Following is a list of some such theorems, numbered for reference, which are of interest for various reasons. (They do not all begin with "C" and hence do not all purport to represent valid deductions.) The reader should carry out the calculations.[8] He should also consider whether propositions of the forms in question seem to be logically true and whether arguments so represented seem to be deductively valid. With some of these theorems, as for example (4), which commits us to the view that "It's raining" and "It's windy" together entail "It's raining," there seems little apparent difficulty. With others, as for example (13), which commits us to the view that "Brutus killed Caesar" and "It's not the case that Brutus killed Caesar" together entail "Washington was the first President of the United States," we may have difficulties. We shall turn to this case in 9.1. For now it is important mainly to see what issues are at stake. In cases of this sort, it may be that what seems to be so isn't really and that, having now discovered something new about entailment, we had better adjust our thinking accordingly. On the other hand, it may rather be that some step in the argument to this point is faulty, in particular either the assumption that the concepts we are interested in can be treated as truth-functional for present purposes or the assertion that all and only valid arguments depending only on these concepts correspond to tautologous wff's beginning with "C." At least these steps, not to mention representing accurately in the symbolism the form of the proposition expressing the argument, come between calculating the truth table of a wff beginning with "C" and deciding that an argument is or is not valid, and the reader should

[8] For some techniques for shortening the calculating process, see Quine [36], pp. 35ff.

not permit himself to be bullied merely by this parade of formulas certifiable as ttt's.

(1) ApNp   *p ∨ ~ p*
(2) Cpp   *p ⊃ p*
(3) NKpNp   *~ [p ← ~p]*
(4) CKpqp   *[p ⋅ω] ⊃ p*
(5) CpApq   *p ⊃ p ∨ q*
(6) CKApqNpq
(7) CKCpqpq
(8) CKCpqNqNp
(9) CNpCpq
(10) CNpCpNq
(11) CpCqp
(12) CqCNqp
(13) CKpNpq
(14) CqApNp
(15) CCpNpNp
(16) CCNpNqCqp
(17) CCpKqNqNp
(18) CCpCqrCCpqCpr
(19) CCpqCCpCqrCpr
(20) CCpNNqCpq
(21) CCpqCCpNqNp

We also list a few formulas which are *not* theorems but which represent patterns of inference which may sometimes appear to be valid. Reflections like those called for with respect to the theorems would be appropriate with regard to these excluded formulas as well.

    (i)   CKCpqNpNq
    (ii)   CKCpqqp
    (iii)   CKApqpNq

5.7 We have spoken of giving definitions of logical connectives by giving their truth tables, showing how they behave "in use." There is another sense of "definition" which is often very important in logic. It consists in introducing some new symbol and providing that any wff's in which the new symbol occurs can be rewritten in terms of those old symbols which occur in the rewritten version; and any new symbol thus introduced is obviously eliminable, in the sense that anything expressible in the system with it is expressible, perhaps somewhat less perspicuously, without it. Where we are discussing notions defined (in the earlier sense) by truth tables, to say that a given expression containing a new connective is defined (in the present sense) as another expression not containing the new connective, is to say that we propose to write the same column of truth-values under the new connective as appears under the main connective of the expression in terms of which it is being defined.

We thus introduce the connective "E," for which the formation rules are like those for "C," "K," and "A," and which is defined as follows:

E*pq* and KC*pq*C*qp* are equivalent by definition.

Since we can calculate the value of the defining expression, thus:

$$
\begin{array}{c}
\text{K C} p\, q\, \text{C} q\, p \\
\text{t\ \ t\ t\ t\ t\ t\ t} \\
\text{f\ \ f\ t\ f\ t\ f\ t} \\
\text{f\ \ t\ f\ t\ f\ t\ f} \\
\text{t\ \ t\ f\ f\ t\ f\ f,}
\end{array}
$$

we know that wherever we see an "E" we shall assign truth-values under it as they appear under "K" in the above table; that is, when the two wff's it joins have the same truth-value, its value is "t," otherwise, it is "f." We may summarize this information in a truth table for "E,"

$$
\begin{array}{c}
\text{E} p\ q \\
\text{t\ t\ t} \\
\text{f\ t\ f} \\
\text{f\ f\ t} \\
\text{t\ f\ f,}
\end{array}
$$

as long as we are clear that, as we have proceeded, this table was not arrived at in the same way and does not have precisely the same status as our earlier "defining" truth tables. (Another possible definition of "E" is to define E*pq* as AK*pq*KN*p*N*q*.)

The question arises as to how we are to read wff's in which "E" occurs. The usual reading is "is equivalent to" for the obvious reason that two propositions stand in this relation if and only if they have equivalent truth-values. "If and only if," which is simply a way of reading off the defining expression, "C*qp*" amounting to "*p* if *q*" and "C*pq*" amounting to "*p* only if *q*," is preferable, however. The latter reading preserves a distinction between expressions which when combined with others make larger expressions (as, for instance, "or," "and," "not," and "if . . . then") and expressions which say something about other expressions (as, for instance, "alternates with," "is conjoined with," "is false," and "implies").[9] Another way of saying the same thing is to contrast the **use** of an expression (in "It's not the case that it's raining," the expression "it's raining" is *used*) with its **mention**

---

[9] See Quine [35], pp. 23–33, for a discussion of these issues.

(in " 'It's raining' is false," the expression "it's raining" is *mentioned*). (Failure to observe this distinction can lead to considerable confusion, as we shall see presently.) Since we have been treating our connectives so far as expressions of the former kind, we shall continue to do so and read "E*pq*" as "*p* if and only if *q*."

Here again there is a dimension of convention in our readings, and we can certainly introduce any symbols we like with any truth tables we like. But it should be clear that associating this new connective with the concept "if and only if" raises precisely the same kinds of questions as the association of our previous connectives with their respective concepts.

Given the requirements of this kind of definition, it is clear that we could have defined some of our original connectives in terms of one another and had them behave in the same way as they now behave, having been introduced separately. Thus to define "C," for example, we have only to look for an expression containing two proposition stand-ins but not containing "C" which has the same main column of truth-values as C*pq*. We have not far to look. C*pq* may be defined as NK*p*N*q* or as AN*pq*. Similarly "A" and "K" may be defined in terms of one another. A*pq* may be defined as NKN*p*N*q*; alternatively (*not* simultaneously — why not?), K*pq* may be defined as NAN*p*N*q*. (These relations would *not* hold between conjunction and *exclusive* disjunction, which is one reason to introduce inclusive disjunction first. We can, however, define exclusive disjunction in terms of the connectives available. See 5.8 below.)

This kind of thing can be pushed to the point where, if we are willing to begin with a connective which has no immediate counterpart in ordinary discourse, we can define *all* of the connectives so far discussed in terms of it.[10] We designate the connective by "S" and give its truth table as follows:

$$\begin{array}{ccc} \text{S} & p & q \\ \text{f} & \text{t} & \text{t} \\ \text{t} & \text{t} & \text{f} \\ \text{t} & \text{f} & \text{t} \\ \text{t} & \text{f} & \text{f} \end{array}$$

The same end can be achieved with a different connective, defined as follows:

[10] This discovery is also apparently due to Peirce. See [31], 4.12ff, 4.264ff. It is usually credited to Sheffer, who apparently rediscovered it independently some years later. See [22], p. 423.

$$D\,p\,q$$
f t t
f t f
f f t
t f f

The reader is invited to construct the required definitions.

The point of thus attempting interdefinitions of connectives is at least twofold. Insofar as it suggests interrelationships between the connectives we are studying, it contributes to our primary aims. To understand these interrelationships is to understand more than if we worked with each connective separately. More important, in the kind of work done with logical systems once they have been constructed (and apart from questions of interpretation), it is often convenient to have as few **primitive notions** (that is, notions *not* defined and introduced in terms of others *within the system*) as possible.

When a theorem begins with "E," it can be interpreted, with all the provisos which go with all such interpretations, as claiming that propositions of the forms represented by the two wff's joined by the "E" entail one another. (Why?) This, in turn, has often been interpreted as the claim that the two are logically equivalent or "mean the same thing." These remarks will provide the reader with a way of seeing and testing informally the claims which these theorems may be thought to involve. We conclude this section, then, by listing some theorems which employ the "E" and which could, of course, be written without it.[11] Here and henceforth when we list theorems, we continue numbering from the end of the preceding list.

(22) EAppp	(30) EKpqKqp
(23) EANpNqNKpq	(31) EApKqrKApqApr
(24) EKNpNqNApq	(32) EKpAqrAKpqKpr
(25) EpNNp	(33) ECpqCNqNp
(26) EKppp	(34) EKpKqrKKpqr
(27) ECpqANpq	(35) EApAqrAApqr
(28) ECpqNKpNq	(36) EEpqEqp
(29) EApqAqp	

[11] The theorems given in this section are subject to a different interpretation from that which we have given them. In this different interpretation they give us information not about the truth-values of propositions but about classes and their members. The result is what is known as Boolean algebra. See Kneale and Kneale [22], pp. 404–427, and Strawson [45], Ch. 4.

5.8 With a fair sample of the entailment claims in behalf of which the present system can be invoked before us, let us return to questions about the adequacy of our system.

The first point to be noticed is that a great many propositions which do not at first glance seem to involve the concepts represented can in fact be regarded as involving them. For example, many cases where "not" appears not to be a propositional connective, for example, "Tom is not bald" can be paraphrased in such a way that "not" does appear as a propositional connective. In this case, an obvious paraphrase is "It is not the case that Tom is bald." Similarly, with occurrences of "and" to link subjects or predicates, such as "Tom and Jim are seniors" and "Tom is football captain and baseball captain," paraphrases are available which make "and" a propositional connective: "Tom is a senior and Jim is a senior" and "Tom is football captain and Tom is baseball captain." What of "Tom and Jim are cousins"? Here it must be recognized that "and" is not performing, even implicitly, the function of a propositional connective joining "Tom is a cousin" and "Jim is a cousin," for the original proposition presumably asserts that they are cousins of *one another*, which the proposed paraphrase does not. This kind of proposition cannot be dealt with until we develop the equipment to analyze the *internal* forms of propositions, in 10.3.

Examples of these kinds illustrate a general point which may be put thus: **grammatical form** is often misleading as to logical form.[12] I shall not pause to specify the notion of grammatical form, but one of our examples will illustrate the distinction suggested here. The sentence-type "Tom and Jim are seniors" is not a compound of two sentence-types. Our analysis of the proposition which this sentence-type would normally be used to express, however, an analysis which is intended to reveal its logical form, its "form" in the sense discussed in 3.3, suggests that that proposition is a compound of two propositions conjoined by the concept "and." Conversely, we have suggested, the proposition normally expressed by the sentence-type "Tom and Jim are cousins" does not, contrary to appearances, involve the concept "and" at all. In the first case we can, contrary to "grammatical" appearances, analyze a proposition as involving one of the concepts

---

[12] This formula summarizes the impulse behind much of the early work of Russell. See, for example, Russell [41], Lecture II.

we set out to represent in our system; in the second, equally contrary to appearances, we cannot. There are no rules for finding the logical form of a proposition beneath the grammatical form of a sentence-type; what is needed is a sensitivity to the many ways in which a single concept can be given linguistic clothing, and this is more a matter of understanding the language we speak than of knowing the logical features of such concepts as "and."

Another fact which facilitates our dealing with apparently different concepts in terms of our limited set of notions is that there are cases where differences important for some purposes may be ignored and apparently different connective concepts collapsed into one. For example, "Tom is strong but Tom is slow" and "Tom is strong; nevertheless, Tom is fast" can be paraphrased respectively as "Tom is strong and Tom is slow" and "Tom is strong and Tom is fast," for the essential purport of these propositions seems to be expressed by these conjunctions. What is suggested in addition by the use of "but" (that we might wish Tom to be fast as well) and by the use of "nevertheless" (that we might not expect Tom to be fast as well) may be regarded as irrelevant to logical relations of inferability from the *proposition* expressed (although we might infer something about the speaker from the way in which he expressed this proposition.)

Similar points may be made about any one of a number of ways of expressing a proposition which can be regarded for certain purposes as equivalent to "If this litmus paper is placed in acid, then it turns red."

   (i)   This litmus paper turns red if it is placed in acid.
   (ii) This litmus paper has been placed in acid only if it turns red.
   (iii) This litmus paper's being placed in acid is a sufficient condition of its turning red.
   (iv) This litmus paper's turning red is a necessary condition of its having been placed in acid.
   (v)   "This litmus paper is placed in acid" implies "This litmus paper turns red."
   (vi) This litmus paper has been placed in acid; therefore it has turned red.
   (vii) Because this litmus paper has been placed in acid, it has turned red.

There are many differences among these locutions. For example, (iii) and (iv) express matters in such a way that the assertion is made explicitly by asserting that there is what might be called a connection between facts (such as the fact of the litmus paper's being placed in acid.) In (v) the claim appears as one about connections between propositions. In (vi) and (vii), besides any claims which may be made explicitly or implicitly about connections, the antecedent and consequent are apparently asserted. Again these differences appear irrelevant to logical relations of entailment among propositions of this sort, except for the difference in (vi) and (vii), which can be represented, if necessary, by simply conjoining the assertion of antecedent and consequent to the assertion of the conditional.

An apparent conditional, like "If something is dropped, then it falls," while involving the notion "if . . . then," requires more for its analysis. Such **open conditionals** are dealt with briefly in 10.5. (In fact, for many purposes, examples like our litmus paper example, especially if the "this" is dropped so that they become general, can best be analyzed in the manner there outlined.) Other apparent conditionals, such as "If he was a great politician, still he was no statesman," and "If you ask me, he was a poor politician, too," seem not to involve at all the concept "if . . . then" which we are studying.

The remarks made so far bear on the problem of recognizing, in the face of often misleading grammatical clues, whether and how the concepts we set out to study occur. We must now consider the more basic question whether our formal counterparts of these concepts are adequate for our purposes. We can pose this question by giving a few instances of cases where logical relationships appear to hold in ways different from the ways in which our theorems claim that they hold.

(i) "If either Tom is a boy or Tom is a girl and Tom is a boy, then it's not the case that Tom is a girl" appears to be a logical truth, but the wff which would seem to represent its form, "CKApqpNq," is not a theorem.

(ii) "They got married and had a baby if and only if they had a baby and got married" does not appear to be a logical truth, but the wff which would seem to represent its form, "EKpqKqp," is a theorem.

(iii) "If Washington was the first President of the United States, then if the moon is made of green cheese Washington was the first President of the United States" does not appear to be a logical truth, but the wff which would seem to represent its form, "CpCqp," is a theorem.

The replies which can be given to these challenges will illustrate the kinds of moves that are available to the defender of the adequacy of a given systematic representation of a concept. As to the first, the reply takes the form of arguing that this logical truth depends on the occurrence of an *exclusive* "or," whereas the "A" is meant to represent an *inclusive* "or," but we can still deal with the case, as suggested in our discussion of the exclusive "or" in 5.5, by defining the concept in terms of those already available. Where it is thought to be important to preserve the exclusive force of "or," as in showing that the proposition mentioned in (i) above is a logical truth, we can express the force of the first conjunct of the antecedent as "Either Tom is a boy or Tom is a girl, and it's not the case both that Tom is a boy and Tom is a girl." In this paraphrase all the connectives can be understood as the truth-functional connectives already discussed, and the wff which now represents the logical form of the original proposition, "CKKApqNKpqpNq," is a theorem. (Alternatively one may regard "or" as having an inclusive sense even in the original proposition and the implied "exclusivity" as being a consequence of a connection between the meanings of the actual propositions involved. In this case the proposition would not be true in virtue of its form, at least not on any analysis of form available to us at this point. Then the fact that the original representative of the form of the proposition, "CKApqpNq," is not a theorem would not be an embarrassment.)

As regards the second challenge, the issue concerns the apparent implication of temporal priority in the "and" which makes "They got married and had a baby" far from equivalent to "They had a baby and got married." Here we could argue that this "and" was simply a different concept from that we have represented; we could at the same time argue that part of that concept was our truth-functional "and." Thus "They got married and had a baby" could be paraphrased, still using the truth-functional "and," as "They got married and they had a baby and they got married before they had a baby," while "They had a baby and got married" could similarly be paraphrased as "They had a baby and they got married and they had a baby before they got married." Now the forms of these propositions could be represented, given our available tools, as "KKpqr" and "KKqps," and "EKKpqrKKqps" is not a theorem. Our strategy involved arguing that the concept involved is not the one we are trying to represent but is in part "made up" of it and then paraphrasing so that the "excess meaning" of the concept appears in a separate proposition. The danger here is that just that part of the concept which is relevant to most of the interesting entailments involving it may disappear into the unanalyzed proposition tacked on at the end of our paraphrase.

This danger becomes obvious when we try to deal with our third challenge. It might be argued that "If Washington was the first President of the United States, then if the moon is made of green cheese Washington was the first President of the United States" is indeed logically true. What is not is the stronger claim which might be made if the second "if . . . then" is understood as asserting some stronger connection of some kind between the moon's being made of green cheese and Washington's being the first President of the United States. What is not a logical truth, then, and to which, as we desire, no theorem corresponds, is something like "If Washington was the first President of the United States, then if the moon is made of green cheese Washington was the first President of the United States, and there is a connection between the moon's being made of green cheese and Washington's being the first President of the United States." Here the "if . . . then's" could still be understood in our truth-functional sense, and the wff which might represent the form of the proposition as paraphrased, "CpKCqpr," is not a theorem.

At this point, however, we will be tempted to say that it is precisely the connection which is at issue when we consider what is asserted or entailed by an "if . . . then" proposition. To put this assertion of connection in some separate unanalyzed proposition is to extract and leave unanalyzed a crucial part of the force of most conditional propositions, even if the bare truth-functional notion is a part of that force as well. Claiming that part of the force of a conditional is the assertion that there is a connection between antecedent and consequent directly involves claiming that conditionals are not truth-functionally analyzable, of course, as brief reflection on the notion of truth-functionality should show. In the face of this intractability of conditionals to truth-functional analysis one can simply say that the analysis is not intended to deal with some conditionals (or a part of the force of most conditionals). This kind of response involves giving up some of the claims about the scope of our system, however. To respond this way too often would be to purchase the adequacy of our formal notions to the concepts they represent at the cost of making these concepts ones which far from exhaust the logically relevant ways of connecting propositions to form complex propositions.[13]

We have observed varying tactics which can be used in harmonizing apparent logical truths with the claims sanctioned by our system. Some of these tactics seem to suggest that the system can do more than at first appears, others, that claims in behalf of the system must be carefully restricted. In this latter kind of situation the problems arise precisely where some connection, such as temporal precedence or causality, seems to be part of the force of the concept we set out to represent, a connection which by definition cannot be captured if we regard the connective as truth-functional.[14]

[13] See Chisholm in Feigl and Sellars [13] for a presentation of some reasons for believing that so-called "contrary-to-fact" conditionals resist truth-functional analysis.

[14] For a strong attack on the thesis that the concepts we are trying to represent are truth-functional, see Strawson, Selection 16, in Iseminger [21]. For a defense of the truth-functionality of the conditional, a view with a long history (see Kneale and Kneale [22], pp. 128ff), see Faris, Selection 17 in Iseminger [21]. The thesis not only that these connectives are truth-functional, but also that all significant contexts in which propositions can occur are truth-functional, was once maintained by Wittgenstein. See [50], 5.3. For some of the difficulties it raises, see Pitcher [32], pp. 56–68.

6

Axiomatic deduction

6.1 We now turn to a different way of arriving at the same system (in the sense of the same set of theorems) as that yielded by the truth table testing method. This system will be one way of formulating what is known as the **propositional calculus.** The truth table method provides us with what is called a **decision procedure**, that is to say, a method whereby, given a wff as a candidate to be a theorem, it is possible to discover by a simple "mechanical" procedure, in a finite number of steps, whether or not it is a theorem. The method we are about to discuss is a variant of the **deductive** method of developing logical systems, with which most readers should be at least vaguely acquainted from studying geometry. This method provides us with a way of selecting theorems by taking some of the theorems as **axioms** and constructing **proofs** of other theorems by deriving them from the axioms according to specified **transformation rules**. (As the terms are used here, the axioms are included among the theorems; this is not true of all uses of the terms.)

If our present aim is to have a deductive system with the same theorems as the system developed by means of truth tables, the axioms must first of all be ttt's. The other requirement is simply that we in fact be able to deduce all and only ttt's from our axioms using our specified rules. (We must be careful, by the way, not to confuse our transformation rules with the principles of entailment or deductive inference which we want our theorems to embody. The former tell us what we can do with wff's in a formal system; the latter tell us what we can validly infer from given propositions. The term "transformation

45

rule" is well suited to emphasize that the rules in our system are rules for the manipulation of symbols. Nevertheless, a little reflection should show that the moves our intra-systematic rules permit us to make will be moves between wff's which, under interpretation, represent forms of propositions which do stand in an entailment relation.) The development of our system, then, will consist of the application of the rules to our axioms so as to construct proofs of other theorems.

It is worth observing that the deductive method will suffer from a defect from which the testing method is free. The test, such as the truth table, provides us with a way of telling quite simply *whether or not* a wff is a theorem; deducing or proving a wff will show us that it *is* a theorem, but failing to prove a wff does not show that it is *not* a theorem. Our ingenuity may simply have failed. In view of this fact, it might be asked why we add this apparently weaker way of doing things to the way we already have. The answer is twofold. First, to see how some theorems can be deduced from others provides us with a sense of "logical order" which we cannot get from merely testing them one after another. Instead of a heap of theorems we have a structure made up of them. More important, there is a sense in which the deductive method is *more* powerful, for it is often difficult and even theoretically impossible to discover in areas of logic other than the propositional calculus a decision procedure analogous to truth tables. In these instances we must rely on the deductive method to achieve any sort of principle for sorting out the theorems from the other wff's, and it is well to understand the method by first investigating a fairly simple application of it in an area of logic with which we are already familiar.

I have described our present task as that of developing a deductive system whose theorems are all and only ttt's. It is important to remember, though, that deductive systems can be developed without respect to their interpretation; we need have no predetermined idea of what we want to turn out to be theorems. We may simply take some axioms and rules and see what follows. On the other hand, the theorems we derive deductively need not be related to concepts in ordinary use through some intermediate such as the truth table system; one might discover them deductively and relate them to ordinary concepts directly, much as we did (or suggested that the reader do) with our ttt's. Our job will be simpler in the present context, however, if we regard it as the deductive development of a system whose theorems are all ttt's and only ttt's. The eventual *proof* that our system meets this test is a matter of **metatheory,** proving things about systems rather than within them, to which we shall turn in Chapter 8.

6.2 We begin by adopting the same formation rules as those given in 5.3. Rather than giving axioms directly, it is more convenient to give **axiom schemata,** employing metavariables, which provide in effect that each of the infinite number of wff's of the form of a given schema is an axiom. For example, our axiom schema

A1. C*pp*

provides that "Cqq," "CCpqCpq," "CKCpqApqKCpqApq," among other wff's, are all axioms. In order to see whether a wff is an axiom according to a given schema, see if it is possible to arrive at the wff by substituting some one wff for each occurrence of a given metavariable throughout the axiom schema. Our other axiom schemata are as follows:

A2. C*p*C*qp*
A3. CC*pq*CC*p*C*qr*C*pr*
A4. CC*p*NN*q*C*pq*
A5. CC*pq*CC*p*N*q*N*p*

The reader should convince himself that all the axioms, however complex, provided by these schemata would be ttt's. (Compare them with theorems (2), (11), (19), (20), and (21) in 5.6.)

Since, however, these axiom schemata in effect give us only the properties of "C" and "N," we must introduce our other constants by definition, as we did with "E" in 5.7, or else ttt's involving "K," "A," and "E" will not be provable. This we do as follows:

D1. A*pq* and CN*pq* are equivalent by definition.
D2. K*pq* and NC*p*N*q* are equivalent by definition.
D3. E*pq* and NCC*pq*NC*qp* are equivalent by definition.

The expressions said to be equivalent by definition can be tested for identity of main rows of truth tables which, given our aims, is a necessary condition of the adequacy of the definitions.

We can now state our transformation rules, using metavariables, of course.

R1. Given two steps, C*pq* and *p*, it is permissible to write down *q*.
R2. Given a step *p* it is permissible to write down *q*, where *q* is the result of substituting for any (proper or improper) part of *p* which is itself a wff another wff equivalent by definition to that part. (An improper part of *p* is *p* itself; a proper part is any smaller segment of *p*.)

With these elements we can construct proofs, sequences of wff's such that each wff is an axiom or can be obtained from a previous step or previous steps as provided by one of the transformation rules. Any step in a proof will be a theorem, although we are usually interested primarily in the last step, and, if our system succeeds in its aim, a wff will be a theorem if and only if it is a ttt.

6.3 We may illustrate the derivation of theorems by giving a proof of our earlier theorem (15). To the right of each step will be an indication of the right by which it appears in a proof, which axiom schema it is an instance of, if it is an instance of an axiom schema, which preceding step or steps it is derived from and according to what rule, if it is derived from preceding steps according to one of the rules (together with an indication of which definition is being appealed to if R2 is being invoked.)

1) CCppCCpNpNp   A5
2) Cpp   A1
3) CCpNpNp   R1, 1), 2)

Note that 1) is in fact an instance of axiom schema A5, the special case where "p" is substituted for both *p* and *q* in the schema. Such special cases are often useful in constructing proofs.[1]

The reader should be able to determine easily enough that this is a proof by the criteria given. (He should also be able to see that each step is a ttt; so far, so good.) But it is not easy to see how one would go about discovering a proof for a given theorem. The only strategy available, really, is to try to get some steps *p* and C*pq* established where what we are interested in establishing is *q*, or, if our theorem contains constants other than "C" and "N," some wff which follows from *q* by R2. R1 will then provide us with *q* and then, if necessary, R2 will yield the desired theorem. But this is all much more easily said than done.

[1] For further illustrations of proofs in a deductive development of the propositional calculus, see Nidditch [29].

It is easy enough to write down axioms and apply rules to them and thus construct perfectly good proofs; it is equally easy to work back from the desired theorem to see what it would follow from. It is not so easy to make these processes meet in the middle of a proof. Often nothing but a great deal of random tinkering will yield the desired result.

Furthermore, it is often the case that in constructing proofs it would be convenient to appeal to theorems already proved. In general such shortcuts are permitted; one simply writes down theorems already proved, with the understanding that, by reference to its proof, a proof which exactly fulfilled the criteria given could be constructed on demand. Still, this makes a problem of the form "Construct a proof of p" that much more difficult, for it may be that in constructing a proof of p one must prove most of the interesting theorems of propositional logic. These difficulties in discovering proofs could partly be met by simply adding on axioms and transformation rules when one got tired (making sure, of course, that they fulfilled the criteria we have mentioned for such axioms and rules.) But the economy of basic principles which our system exhibits would be sacrificed, and this economy, besides showing how little one need start with in developing the whole body of propositional logic, is extremely useful when we come to prove the identity of our system with that given by the truth table test.

6.4 Having convinced the reader that the discovery of proofs in the present system is a difficult matter, I have done all I wished to do here. If he is not yet convinced, he can write down any arbitrarily selected ttt and set out to construct a proof of it. Without ourselves constructing any more proofs in this system, we shall in Chapter 8 sketch a proof that all and only ttt's can be proved. I want to turn now, however, to a way of developing propositional logic which provides relatively easy and automatic strategies for discovering proofs of arbitrarily selected ttt's. With the difficulties we have just seen in mind, the reader will be able to see why the method used in the next chapter has been called **natural deduction.**

7

Natural deduction

7.1 What mainly distinguishes natural deduction systems from axiomatic systems is that natural deduction systems have no axioms. Since axioms both give the basic properties of the connectives which occur in them and provide us with something to start with in constructing proofs, we must find other ways of performing these two tasks in natural deduction systems. As for the first, natural deduction systems characteristically define connectives (in the sense in which truth tables and axioms provide definitions) by giving rules which state how wff's having these connectives as main connectives can appear in proofs: a rule, called an **introduction rule**, which says when we can write down such wff's, and a rule, called an **elimination rule**, which says what we can write down given such wff's. As for the second, our rules will provide ways of writing down steps to begin proofs without making any unjustified claims about the provability of these steps and ways of deriving theorems *de novo*, without starting with any axioms. How our rules enable us to do these things we shall see.[1]

7.2 Having again adopted the symbols and formation rules of 5.3, we turn to the introduction and elimination rules for "K." The introduction rule states that we may infer Kpq or Kqp from p and q separately. The elimination rule states that from Kpq we may infer p and we may also infer q.

---

[1] Pioneer work in natural deduction techniques may be seen in Gentzen [17]. Fitch [14], on which many parts of the present book are based, is a textbook employing these techniques. A more recent such book is Anderson and Johnstone [3].

We may represent these rules schematically as follows:

(KI)

·	·	·
·	·	·
k	p	Ri
·	·	·
·	·	·
l	q	Rj
·	·	·
·	·	·
m	Kpq	KI, k, l
·	·	·
·	·	·
n	Kqp	KI, l, k
·	·	·
·	·	·

(KE)

·	·	·
·	·	·
l	Kpq	Ri
·	·	·
·	·	·
m	p	KE, l
·	·	·
·	·	·
n	q	KE, l
·	·	·
·	·	·

Here and in the schematic representations of rules which appear in what follows, the vertical line signifies that this is a proof; the italic letters to the left of the line are schematic representations of the numbers assigned to the steps in the proof; the designations to the right of the proof are schemata for indicating the justifications of these steps, "Ri" and "Rj" indicating simply that the steps in question are justified by some rule, which one does not matter in the present context, the others indicating how a step's being justified by the rule represented is shown in a proof and indicating the step or steps from which it is derived; the dots indicate that steps need not be adjacent and may occur anywhere in a proof, although, of course, the step or steps being appealed to must occur before they are used to justify a step. In these rules, but not in all of our rules, it can be seen that more than one step may be justified by a given rule from a certain preceding step or steps. In such cases, any of the steps which may follow may be written down alone or all of them in any order.

For our purposes the ultimate justification of choosing these rules will be that they will enable us to prove all and only ttt's as theorems; nonetheless, reflections like those in terms of which the defining truth tables for these connectives were rendered plausible would be worthwhile and would serve the same ends here and with regard to the rules which are to be given.

We can see how these rules would work in practice if we imagine that in working out a proof we are required to move from a step "KKpqr" to a step "KpKqr."

(i)

.	.	.
.	.	.
n	KKpqr	Ri
$n + 1$	Kpq	KE, n
$n + 2$	r	KE, n
$n + 3$	p	KE, $n + 1$
$n + 4$	q	KE, $n + 1$
$n + 5$	Kqr	KI, $n + 4$, $n + 2$
$n + 6$	KpKqr	KI, $n + 3$, $n + 5$
.	.	.
.	.	.

54 AN INTRODUCTION TO DEDUCTIVE LOGIC

This example illustrates, however, that we have as yet not found a rule which does the second job of axioms. We have not as yet defined the notion of proof for this system, but it should be clear that it will be something like the definition in 6.2, in that every step will have to be justifiable in some way. So far a series of rules like KI and KE will only permit us to write down strings of wff's in which at least the first step will have a designation like "R*i*," which means that it is as yet unjustified.

A possible move here would simply be to allow the writing down as **hypotheses** any step or steps we wished. Then the section of proof above, which showed that we could get from "KKpqr" to "KpKqr," could be written as a proof in its own right as follows:

(ii)	1	KKpqr	hypothesis
	2	Kpq	KE, 1
	3	r	KE, 1
	4	p	KE, 2
	5	q	KE, 2
	6	Kqr	KI, 5, 3
	7	KpKqr	KI, 4, 6

If we allow this to be a proof, of course, we shall not be able to say that every step in a proof is a theorem, for none of these steps is a ttt, and so, if we want our theorems all to be ttt's, none of these steps can be a theorem. Nonetheless, it is clear that the fact that we can get from step 1 to step 7 can be interpreted as telling us something about entailment. We would be able to deduce a proposition of the form representable by 7 from a proposition of the form representable by 1, as reflections on propositions whose forms could be represented by these wff's should make seem quite reasonable. It would be possible to develop the theory of entailments involving propositional connectives in these terms, showing that an entailment holds by getting from something representing the entailer to something representing the entailed.[2]

We have already decided, however, to turn such questions into questions about theorems beginning with "C." Hence the question

[2] Suppes [46] is an example of a book which mainly deals with entailments in this way.

becomes one of finding the right rule for introducing the "C." If a proposition whose form is representable by step 7 is entailed by a proposition whose form is representable by step 1, then the wff made up of "C" followed by 1 followed by 7 should be a ttt. (See that it is; compare also theorem (34).) So we shall want it to be a theorem in our present system. Stated generally, the information we get about entailment from a "proof" such as (ii) can be expressed in terms of theorems by saying that when we can get from p alone to q we want Cpq to be a theorem.

7.3 With this much by way of motivation, we may schematize our rule of CI thus:

(CI)

l	p	HP(CI)
m	q	Ri
n	Cpq	CI, l—m

Applying it in the situation represented by (ii) gives us the following:

(iii)

1	KKpqr	HP(CI)
2	Kpq	KE, 1
3	r	KE, 1
4	p	KE, 2
5	q	KE, 2
6	Kqr	KI, 5, 3
7	KpKqr	KI, 4, 6
8	CKKpqrKpKqr	CI, 1–7

In explaining and commenting on this schema and its application, it will be necessary to introduce terminology which will be used throughout the remainder of this book.

We begin by defining a proof in this system as a sequence of wff's such that each of them either follows from a preceding step (or steps) or is a hypothesis. In a rule such as CI it is the whole process of getting from p to q which justifies us in writing down Cpq. This whole sequence l—m (in (iii), 1–7), beginning with a single hypothesis, is called a **subordinate proof**. It is set in to the right with its own vertical line, and the short horizontal line indicates that the step above that line is a hypothesis. It is said to be **subordinate to** any other proof whose vertical line would be intersected by a line drawn horizontally to the left from the vertical line indicating the subordinate proof in question through the left-most vertical line. (A subordinate proof must be subordinate to at least one proof.) It is **immediately subordinate to** the proof indicated by the first vertical line thus intersected.

With regard to hypotheses, it will be simpler for our present purposes if we do not allow "proofs" like (ii) in 7.2 and stipulate that all and only subordinate proofs have hypotheses (this requirement that a subordinate proof have a hypothesis will be modified in connection with rules introduced in Chapters 9 and 11), and they must have exactly one. We shall indicate the rule for which the subordinate proof is to be developed after the "HP" which we put to the right of its hypothesis. Being able to write down a hypothesis gives us the necessary "something to begin with" in constructing proofs. Note that, although in a sense we can write down any wff we please as a hypothesis, the one we do write down will be strictly determined by what we are trying to derive; in the present case it will be the first wff joined by "C" in the wff we are trying to get by CI.

We now define a *theorem* as, not any step in a proof, but rather any step immediately to the right of the left-most vertical line of a proof. Step 8 in (iii), and only step 8, is a theorem, which is as we wish it. This step comes to be a theorem on this criterion because in writing down a step by CI we move out to the proof to which the proof we appeal to is immediately subordinate. This move shows that, in writing down Cpq, we are in no sense "assuming" p; we are rather appealing to the whole process of getting from p to q. We can also see that the freedom to hypothesize anything we wish does not make it possible to prove any wff at all as a theorem. (Why not?)

It is often necessary to have subordinate proofs nested in other subordinate proofs. For example, if we have reached a stage in a proof in which we want to get from step "r" to step "CpCqr," we would proceed to set up a CI proof thus, where the question mark indicates that we are not yet sure how to get the step thus designated:

$$
\begin{array}{lll}
\cdot & \cdot & \cdot \\
\cdot & \cdot & \cdot \\
n & r & \mathrm{R}i \\
n+1 & \quad p & \mathrm{HP(CI)} \\
\cdot & \quad \cdot & \cdot \\
\cdot & \quad \cdot & \cdot \\
\cdot & \quad \cdot & \cdot \\
m & \quad \mathrm{Cqr} & ? \\
m+1 & \mathrm{CpCqr} & \mathrm{CI},\ (n+1)\text{---}m \\
\cdot & \cdot & \cdot \\
\cdot & \cdot & \cdot
\end{array}
$$

To get step m would require another subordinate CI proof, thus:

$$
\begin{array}{lll}
\cdot & \cdot & \cdot \\
\cdot & \cdot & \cdot \\
n & r & \mathrm{R}i \\
n+1 & \quad p & \mathrm{HP(CI)} \\
n+2 & \quad\quad q & \mathrm{HP(CI)} \\
\cdot & \quad\quad \cdot & \cdot \\
\cdot & \quad\quad \cdot & \cdot \\
\cdot & \quad\quad \cdot & \cdot \\
m-1 & \quad\quad r & ? \\
m & \quad \mathrm{Cqr} & \mathrm{CI},\ (n+2)\text{---}(m-1) \\
m+1 & \mathrm{CpCqr} & \mathrm{CI},\ (n+1)\text{---}m \\
\cdot & \cdot & \cdot \\
\cdot & \cdot & \cdot
\end{array}
$$

To complete the proof we must get "r." To get it, we reflect that all of these maneuvers are taking place under the supposition that "r" has already been established. For this reason we permit the **borrowing** into a subordinate proof of any step already written down in a proof to which the subordinate proof is subordinate. The passage we were just considering may then be completed as follows:

n	r	Ri
$n + 1$	p	HP(CI)
$n + 2$	q	HP(CI)
$n + 3$	r	B, n
$n + 4$	Cqr	CI, $(n + 2)$—$(n + 3)$
$n + 5$	CpCqr	CI, $(n + 1)$—$(n + 4)$

Those who are disturbed by the question in what sense we may be said to have "derived" "r" from "q" should recall that the "C" is to represent the truth-functional "if . . . then," and no entailment claim is involved when the step, as $n + 4$, is not a theorem. A rule for CI which intends to capture the truth-functional "if . . . then" should permit us precisely to write down Cpq when we have already written down q. (Why?) The "intuitive" justification for CI where it is being used to write down some step not a theorem is thus different from where it is being used to write down a theorem, just as the "C" has a different import where it begins a theorem and where it does not.

Before proceeding to discuss strategies for constructing proofs of theorems involving "C" and "K," we must give the schema for the rule CE.

(CE)

```
  ·  │ ·              ·
  ·  │ ·              ·
  l  │ Cpq            Ri
  ·  │ ·              ·
  ·  │ ·              ·
  m  │ p              Rj
  ·  │ ·              ·
  ·  │ ·              ·
  n  │ q              CE, l, m
  ·  │ ·              ·
  ·  │ ·              ·
```

It is clear that we want the order of steps l and m to be irrelevant to the application of this rule. We could state another version of the rule to accommodate this fact. In practice we shall be relatively informal here and regard the rule as stated as covering the case where l and m are reversed as well. We shall do likewise in similar cases in which more than one premise is required for the application of the rule.

Let us now turn to a proof of our earlier theorem

$$(18) \quad CCpCqrCCpqCpr.$$

The strategy in constructing a proof is to play both ends against the middle, looking at what needs to be derived and seeing what introduction rule will yield it and repeating this process as many times as possible, and then turning to what we have to work from, borrowing if necessary, and seeing what we can get from it using elimination rules. We can thus build up step by step the end and the beginning of the proof until at some point it becomes possible to see, usually quite easily, how the middle is to be filled in.

The theorem has "C" as its main connective; to prove it we construct a CI proof with the left-hand wff to which the "C" applies as its hypothesis and the right-hand wff to which the "C" applies as its final step:

1	⌐ CpCqr	HP(CI)
.	.	.
.	.	.
n	CCpqCpr	?
$n + 1$	CCpCqrCCpqCpr	CI, 1—n

If we can fill in the gaps between 1 and n successfully, we shall have our proof. The problem reduces to getting from 1 to n. In order to do this we shall require another CI proof, since n begins with a "C."

1	⌐ CpCqr	HP(CI)
2	⌐ Cpq	HP(CI)
.	.	.
.	.	.
$n - 1$	Cpr	?
n	CCpqCpr	CI, 2—$(n - 1)$
$n + 1$	CCpCqrCCpqCpr	CI, 1— n

Now our task reduces to getting from 2 to $n - 1$. Another CI proof is indicated:

1	⌐ CpCqr	HP(CI)
2	⌐ Cpq	HP(CI)
3	⌐ p	HP(CI)
.	.	.
.	.	.
$n - 2$	r	?
$n - 1$	Cpr	CI, 3—$(n - 2)$
n	CCpqCpr	CI, 2—$(n - 1)$
$n + 1$	CCpCqrCCpqCpr	CI, 1—n

At this point no introduction rule will yield $n - 2$, since it consists of a single proposition stand-in. We have now to borrow what we can into the inmost subordinate proof (unless we can see in advance that only certain specific borrowings will be required) and apply appropriate elimination rules to fill in the middle of the proof. In general, the proof can be completed fairly easily once this stage is reached. The completed proof will look like this:

(18)

1	CpCqr	HP(CI)
2	Cpq	HP(CI)
3	p	HP(CI)
4	CpCqr	B, 1
5	Cpq	B, 2
6	Cqr	CE, 3, 4
7	q	CE, 3, 5
8	r	CE, 6, 7
9	Cpr	CI, 3—8
10	CCpqCpr	CI, 2—9
11	CCpCqrCCpqCpr	CI, 1—10

7.4 We now give introduction and elimination rules for "N." The introduction rule is an attempt to capture the idea of negative or indirect proof, which may be stated thus: if we can derive a contradiction from a proposition or derive something which contradicts something else already established, we may assert the negation of that proposition. In representing this rule and future rules having subordinate proofs, we understand subordinate proofs as in 7.3 and permit borrowings under the same circumstances, except when we introduce special kinds of subordinate proofs in Chapters 9 and 11. With regard to NI we could, of course, state another version of the rule to take account of the fact that Nq could equally well occur before q.

(NI)

$$
\begin{array}{lll}
\cdot & \cdot & \cdot \\
\cdot & \cdot & \\
k & p & \mathrm{HP(NI)} \\
\cdot & \cdot & \cdot \\
\cdot & \cdot & \\
l & q & \mathrm{R}i \\
\cdot & \cdot & \cdot \\
\cdot & \cdot & \cdot \\
m & \mathrm{N}q & \mathrm{R}j \\
\cdot & \cdot & \cdot \\
\cdot & \cdot & \\
n & \mathrm{N}p & \mathrm{NI},\ k\text{---}m\ (l,\ m) \\
\cdot & \cdot & \cdot \\
\cdot & \cdot & \\
\end{array}
$$

Here the justification of the step by NI includes reference to the two steps in the subordinate proof of the form q and $\mathrm{N}q$. Although NI will most often involve borrowing one of these steps into the subordinate proof and deriving the other from p, special cases where either l or m is k, or where both l and m are borrowed, are clearly possible and occur fairly frequently. Where the step $\mathrm{N}p$ is a theorem, of course, both q and $\mathrm{N}q$ will have to be derivable from p alone. (Why?) The reader should reflect on the plausibility of the rule and of these special cases, but we shall spend no more time justifying them in terms of the intended interpretation of the connective.

Before turning to proofs involving "N," we must, of course, have an elimination rule. The required rule is called *double* negation elimination.

(NNE)

$$
\begin{array}{lll}
\cdot & \cdot & \cdot \\
\cdot & \cdot & \cdot \\
m & \mathrm{NN}p & \mathrm{R}i \\
\cdot & \cdot & \cdot \\
\cdot & \cdot & \cdot \\
n & p & \mathrm{NNE},\ m \\
\cdot & \cdot & \cdot \\
\cdot & \cdot & \cdot \\
\end{array}
$$

With these two rules we have a kind of universal solvent for deriving steps where no introduction rule will be immediately helpful. If we can get by NI the double negation of the step we want, we can then get that step by NNE. The following pattern occurs frequently in proofs:

$$
\begin{array}{lll}
\vdots & \vdots & \vdots \\
l & Np & \text{HP(NI)} \\
\vdots & \vdots & \vdots \\
m & q & \text{R}i \\
\vdots & \vdots & \vdots \\
n & Nq & \text{R}j \\
n+1 & NNp & \text{NI, } l\!-\!n \ (m, n) \\
n+2 & p & \text{NNE, } n+1 \\
\vdots & \vdots & \vdots
\end{array}
$$

Following are two proofs involving NI and NNE illustrating some of the special cases mentioned. (We will not go through the step by step process of constructing the proof.)

$$
(3) \quad
\begin{array}{lll}
1 & KpNp & \text{HP(NI)} \\
2 & p & \text{KE, 1} \\
3 & Np & \text{KE, 1} \\
4 & NKpNp & \text{NI, 1—3 (2, 3)}
\end{array}
$$

$$
(13) \quad
\begin{array}{lll}
1 & KpNp & \text{HP(CI)} \\
2 & Nq & \text{HP(NI)} \\
3 & KpNp & \text{B, 1} \\
4 & p & \text{KE, 3} \\
5 & Np & \text{KE, 3} \\
6 & NNq & \text{NI, 2—5 (4, 5)} \\
7 & q & \text{NNE, 6} \\
8 & CKpNpq & \text{CI, 1—7}
\end{array}
$$

7.5 We now give schematic representations of the rules for "A" and "E," leaving the question of their plausibility to the reader, then work through a proof involving most of the trickier rules, and finally append a few more proofs of interest for various reasons.

(AI)	·	·		·	(AE)	·	·		·
	·	·		·		·	·		·
l	p		Ri		j	Apq			Rg
	·	·		·		·	·		·
	·	·		·		·	·		·
m	Apq		AI, l		k	$\mid p$			HP(AE)
	·	·		·		·	·		·
	·	·		·		·	·		·
n	Aqp		AI, l		l	$\mid r$			Rh
	·	·		·		·	·		·
	·	·		·		·			
					m	$\mid q$			HP(AE)
					·	·			·
					·	·			·
					·	·			·
					n	$\mid r$			Ri
					·	·			·
					·	·			·
					o	r			AE, j, k—l, m—n
					·	·			·
					·	·			·

Here and in other rules involving two subordinate proofs we could also state a version of the rule in which the other subordinate proof came first.

(EI)

k	p	HP(EI)
l	q	R*i*
m	q	HP(EI)
n	p	R*j*
o	E*pq*	EI, *k—l, m—n*

(EE)

l	E*pq*	R*i*
m	p	R*j*
n	q	EE, *l, m*

also

l	E*pq*	R*i*
m	q	R*j*
n	p	EE, *l, m*

Since the rules for "E" raise no special problems, let us take for a final working through of a proof the theorem

CANpNqNKpq.

The reader, recalling the definition of "E" in 5.7, will recognize that this is, so to speak, "half" of

(23) EANpNqNKpq.

Proving (23) would involve simply combining the proof we are about to see with another one going in the other direction, as it were, and using EI. First, since the main connective is "C," we shall need a CI proof:

$$
\begin{array}{lll}
1 & \quad \text{ANpNq} & \text{HP(CI)} \\
\cdot & \quad \cdot & \cdot \\
\cdot & \quad \cdot & \cdot \\
\cdot & \quad \cdot & \cdot \\
n & \quad \text{NKpq} & ? \\
n+1 & \text{CANpNqNKpq} & \text{CI, } 1\text{—}n
\end{array}
$$

Looking to see how we shall complete the CI proof, we see that alternative tactics are available. Looking at what we must work from suggests AE; looking at what we are working towards suggests NI. Either move will work; since the former turns out to be shorter, we adopt it:

$$
\begin{array}{lll}
1 & \quad \text{ANpNq} & \text{HP(CI)} \\
2 & \quad\quad \text{Np} & \text{HP(AE)} \\
\cdot & \quad\quad \cdot & \cdot \\
\cdot & \quad\quad \cdot & \cdot \\
\cdot & \quad\quad \cdot & \cdot \\
m & \quad\quad \text{NKpq} & ? \\
m+1 & \quad\quad \text{Nq} & \text{HP(AE)} \\
\cdot & \quad\quad \cdot & \cdot \\
\cdot & \quad\quad \cdot & \cdot \\
\cdot & \quad\quad \cdot & \cdot \\
n-1 & \quad\quad \text{NKpq} & ? \\
n & \quad \text{NKpq} & \text{AE, 1, 2—}m\text{, } (m+1)\text{—}(n-1) \\
n+1 & \text{CANpNqNKpq} & \text{CI, } 1\text{—}n
\end{array}
$$

Now it appears that we shall have to use NI in each of the subordinate proofs involved in the use of AE:

1	ANpNq	HP(CI)
2	Np	HP(AE)
3	Kpq	HP(NI)
.	.	.
.	.	.
m	NKpq	NI, 3—? (?, ?)
m + 1	Nq	HP(AE)
m + 2	Kpq	HP(NI)
.	.	.
.	.	.
n − 1	NKpq	NI, (m + 2)—? (?, ?)
n	NKpq	AE, 1, 2—m, (m + 1)—(n − 1)
n + 1	CANpNqNKpq	CI, 1—n

Now we must only get the required contradictions in the NI proofs, which is readily done by means of obvious borrowings and applications of KE, and we have our completed proof:

1	ANpNq	HP(CI)
2	Np	HP(AE)
3	Kpq	HP(NI)
4	Np	B, 2
5	p	KE, 3
6	NKpq	NI, 3—5, (4, 5)
7	Nq	HP(AE)
8	Kpq	HP(NI)
9	Nq	B, 7
10	q	KE, 8
11	NKpq	NI, 8—10, (9, 10)
12	NKpq	AE, 1, 2—6, 7—11
13	CANpNqNKpq	CI, 1—12

We conclude this section by giving several proofs of interest for various reasons, without explaining step by step the strategy required to discover them. There are plenty of proofs left for the reader to discover if he wishes. In general, application of the strategies suggested should make most proofs discoverable as "naturally" as these, but the facts that there are alternatives available and that a bare minimum of ingenuity is required to fill in the middle of a proof should be enough to show that discovering a proof is not merely a mechanical matter in the sense in which truth table testing is.[3] In cases where an impasse is reached in following the obvious strategy, NI, with the contradictory steps gotten in one of the various ways, will often succeed where all else fails. Notice, finally, that once we present a sequence of steps, it *is* a merely mechanical matter to decide whether or not it is a proof. One has simply to see whether or not each step is either a hypothesis in a position where a hypothesis is permissible or is derivable from a previous step or steps according to one of the rules.

(1)	1	NApNp	HP(NI)
	2	p	HP(NI)
	3	ApNp	AI, 2
	4	NApNp	B, 1
	5	Np	NI, 2—4 (3, 4)
	6	ApNp	AI, 5
	7	NNApNp	NI, 1—6 (1, 6)
	8	ApNp	NNE, 7
(2)	1	p	HP(CI)
	2	Cpp	CI, 1—1
(9)	1	Np	HP(CI)
	2	p	HP(CI)
	3	Nq	HP(NI)
	4	Np	B, 1

[3] For techniques like the ones developed here, except that the discovery of proofs *is* a mechanical matter, see the variant of "tree-formed" deduction in Clark and Welsh [9], pp. 99–111.

	5	p	B, 2
	6	NNq	NI, 3—5 (4, 5)
	7	q	NNE, 6
	8	Cpq	CI, 2—7
	9	CNpCpq	CI, 1—8
(11)	1	p	HP(CI)
	2	q	HP(CI)
	3	p	B, 1
	4	Cqp	CI, 2—3
	5	CpCqp	CI, 1—4
(33)	1	Cpq	HP(EI)
	2	Nq	HP(CI)
	3	p	HP(NI)
	4	Cpq	B, 1
	5	q	CE, 3, 4
	6	Nq	B, 2
	7	Np	NI, 3—6 (5, 6)
	8	CNqNp	CI, 2—7
	9	CNqNp	HP(EI)
	10	p	HP(CI)
	11	Nq	HP(NI)
	12	CNqNp	B, 9
	13	Np	CE, 11, 12
	14	p	B, 10
	15	NNq	NI, 11—14 (13, 14)
	16	q	NNE, 15
	17	Cpq	CI, 10—16
	18	ECpqCNqNp	EI, 1—8, 9—17

7.6   It is possible, and for some purposes useful, to effect a reduction in the number of rules taken as primitive by defining (in one sense of that term) a connective in terms of others and then **deriving** its defining (in a different sense of that term) I and E rules.

To derive a rule permitting the passage from p to q is to give a schema for getting from p to q using only rules other than the rule being derived. Having derived the rule, we may then shorten proofs by moving directly from p to q without bothering to write down the intervening steps, always with the understanding that they could be supplied on demand. A derived rule, then, does not permit us to do anything we could not do before, only to do some of the same things more quickly. Thus we can make proofs shorter while at the same time regarding our system, when we wish to, as constituted only by the underived rules. (It is more accurate to redefine "proof" so that only hypotheses and steps following according to underived rules are allowed in a proof and to say that a "proof" using derived rules is only an abbreviation for a genuine proof, where the derivations of the derived rules used provide instructions for constructing the genuine proof.)

We may illustrate the derivation of a rule corresponding to theorem (6), a rule expressing a principle called *modus tollendo ponens* ("the way of affirming by denying"). This rule permits us to move from steps Apq and Np to step q. Since this rule is not an introduction or elimination rule, no recourse to definitions is required here. The derivation is given in metavariables. (Why?)

(*Modus tollendo ponens*)			
	·	·	·
	·	·	·
l	Apq		Ri
	·	·	·
	·	·	·
m	Np		Rj
	·	·	·
	·	·	·
n	p		HP(AE)
$n+1$	Nq		HP(NI)
$n+2$	p		B, n

$n+3$	$\mid$ Np	B, m
$n+4$	NNq	NI, $(n+1)$—$(n+3)[n+2, n+3]$
$n+5$	q	NNE, $n+4$
$n+6$	$\vdash q$	HP(AE)
$n+7$	q	AE, l, n—$(n+5)$, $(n+6)$—$(n+6)$
.	.	.
.	.	.

A number of similar rules, whose derivation will be left to the reader, follow. Note that NE will occur only in subordinate proofs. (Why?)

(*Modus tollens*)

	.	.
	.	.
l	Cpq	Ri
	.	.
	.	.
m	Nq	Rj
	.	.
	.	.
n	Np	MT, l, m
	.	.
	.	.

(Double negation introduction)

	.	.
	.	.
m	p	Ri
	.	.
	.	.
n	NNp	NNI, n
	.	.
	.	.

(Negation
elimination)

$$
\begin{array}{c|cc}
 & \cdot & \cdot \\
 & \cdot & \cdot \\
l & p & R\,i \\
 & \cdot & \cdot \\
 & \cdot & \cdot \\
m & Np & R\,j \\
 & \cdot & \cdot \\
 & \cdot & \cdot \\
n & q & NE,\ l,\ m \\
 & \cdot & \cdot \\
 & \cdot & \cdot \\
\end{array}
$$

In order to derive an introduction rule, we must show how to get from the given step or steps to the defined equivalent of the step beginning with the connective to be introduced. In order to derive an elimination rule, we must get to the desired step from the defined equivalent of the step beginning with the connective to be eliminated. In order to do these things, we shall require definitions, for which we take D1—D3 in 6.2, and a rule of definitional replacement (DR), which will be the same as R2 in 6.2. In order to facilitate comparisons between our axiomatic system and our natural deduction system, we take as underived rules for the natural deduction system CI, CE, NI, NNE, B, and DR. (The reader is invited to investigate other possible combinations of definitions and underived rules to see how to derive the rules which under those conditions need deriving. In general, at least one rule involving subordinate proofs will be required. Why?) We now indicate how to derive I and E rules for the defined connectives under the conditions mentioned. KI and KE are quite straightforward. (We derive only one of the possible conclusions in each case; the other would be readily derivable in analogous fashion.)

(KI)

$$
\begin{array}{c|cc}
 & \cdot & \cdot \\
 & \cdot & \cdot \\
l & p & R\,i \\
 & \cdot & \cdot \\
 & \cdot & \cdot \\
\end{array}
$$

m	q	Rj
	.	.
	.	.
n	CpNq	HP(NI)
$n+1$	p	B, l
$n+2$	q	B, m
$n+3$	Nq	CE, $n, n+1$
$n+4$	NCpNq	NI, $n-(n+3)[n+2, n+3]$
$n+5$	Kpq	DR, $n+4$ (D2)
	.	.
	.	.

(KE)

	.	.
	.	.
l	Kpq	Ri
	.	.
	.	.
m	NCpNq	DR, l (D2)
	.	.
	.	.
n	Nq	HP(NI)
$n+1$	p	HP(CI)
$n+2$	Nq	B, n
$n+3$	CpNq	CI, $(n+1)-(n+2)$
$n+4$	NCpNq	B, m
$n+5$	NNq	NI, $n-(n+4)[n+3, n+4]$
$n+6$	q	NNE, $n+5$
	.	.
	.	.

The derivation of AE is a bit more complicated. The reader should assure himself that it accomplishes what a derivation claims to accomplish: that is, it permits us to replace any use of the rule being derived by a sequence of steps employing only other rules, in this case only "C" and "N" rules, in addition to B and DR (and hypotheses, of course).

(AE)	·	·	·
	·	·	·
j		Apq	Rg
	·	·	·
	·	·	·
k		CNpq	DR, j (D1)
	·	·	·
	·	·	·
l		p	HP(CI)
	·	·	·
	·	·	·
	·	·	·
m		r	Rh
$m+1$		Cpr	CI, l—m
$m+2$		q	HP(CI)
	·	·	·
	·	·	·
	·	·	·
n		r	Ri
$n+1$		Cqr	CI, $(m+2)$—n
$n+2$		Nr	HP(NI)
$n+3$		p	HP(NI)
$n+4$		Cpr	B, $m+1$

$n + 5$		r	CE, $n + 3$, $n + 4$
$n + 6$		Nr	B, $n + 2$
$n + 7$		Np	NI, $(n + 3)$—$(n + 6)[n + 5, n + 6]$
$n + 8$		$CNpq$	B, k
$n + 9$		q	CE, $n + 7$, $n + 8$
$n + 10$		Cqr	B, $n + 1$
$n + 11$		r	CE, $n + 9$, $n + 10$
$n + 12$	NNr		NI, $(n + 2)$—$(n + 11)[n + 2, n + 11]$
$n + 13$	r		NNE, $n + 12$
$\cdot$	$\cdot$		$\cdot$
$\cdot$	$\cdot$		$\cdot$

The reader is left to derive AI and the "E" rules or to experiment, as suggested above, with other combinations of fundamental rules and derivations, according as different connectives are taken as undefined and definitions of the other connectives given in terms of them.

8

Metatheory

8.1 In the last two chapters we have described our task as that of developing deductive systems which had as theorems all ttt's and only ttt's. We now undertake to prove that these aims have been achieved, that our systems, having as theorems all the ttt's, are **complete** and, having only ttt's as theorems, are **consistent**.[1]

These **metatheoretic** proofs about our systems will not be formal in the sense in which proofs within the systems have been, nor will we stop to attend to every detail.[2] (We will make it clear, however, where details are left unattended to.) At times we will regard the systems as constituted only by their basic principles. In the axiomatic system (let us call it System I) these are D1—D3, A1—A5, and R1 and R2; in the natural deduction system (System II), D1—D3, NI, NNE, CI, CE, B, and DR. We will also, when convenient, employ theorems, derived rules, and expressions introduced by definition, although these are, of course, theoretically expendable. The advantages of thus considering the system, now as stripped to its bare essentials, and another time as containing all its resources for convenient operation, will be evident as we proceed.

---

[1] The notions of consistency and completeness are only provisionally characterized here. See 8.3 and 8.5 below for further discussion. With regard to axiomatic developments, a further question is often asked concerning the **independence** of the axioms, that is, the impossibility of deducing any one of them as a theorem given the others. See Hilbert and Ackermann [20], pp. 40–42.

[2] For a discussion of issues raised by the "informality" of metatheoretic proofs, see Quine [35], pp. 319–321.

8.2   As a first step it will be convenient to sketch a proof that Systems I and II are equivalent in the sense of having the same theorems. We will have to show, then, that everything provable in I is provable in II and, conversely, that everything provable in II is provable in I.[3]

To show that everything provable in I is provable in II, it will suffice to show that all the wff's said to be theorems in I by A1—A5 are theorems in II and that we have the force of R1 and R2 in the rules of II. (Why will this suffice?)

We note that theorems of the forms of axiom schemata A1 and A2 have already been proved in II. (They are theorems (2) and (11), as we observed before.) (19)—(21) in 5.7 correspond similarly to A3—A5, although they have not been demonstrated in II. We give a proof of (19) and leave the others to the reader. An exactly corresponding proof could be given of any of the infinite number of wff's which are theorems according to A3, and similarly with regard to the other axiom schemata. (Why?)

1	Cpq		HP(CI)
2	CpNq		HP(CI)
3	p		HP(NI)
4	Cpq		B, 1
5	q		CE, 3, 4
6	CpNq		B, 2
7	Nq		CE, 3, 6
8	Np		NI, 3—7 (5, 7)
9	CCpNqNp		CI, 2—8
10	CCpqCCpNqNp		CI, 1—9

R1 is simply our rule of CE restricted in its application to theorems (since all steps in a proof in I are theorems), so there is no question

---

[3] The overall strategy for this proof of the equivalence of an axiomatic system and a deductive system is derived from Anderson and Belnap [2].

about our having the force of R1 in II. R2 stands in precisely the same relationship to DR. This completes our sketch of the proof that all the theorems in I are provable in II.

Turning to the converse, our strategy will be complicated by the fact that the rules in II involving subordinate proofs have no counterparts in I. What we shall do is give general instructions for eliminating subordinate proofs in a proof in II and show that the result is a proof in I. In order to do this, we shall require the notion of a **quasi-proof** in II, which will be just like a proof in II with the exception that we may introduce axioms of I as steps in an **outermost** proof (that is, a proof subordinate to no other proofs) before the first step of the original proof. This provision will not affect what is provable in II; in order to convert a quasi-proof into a proof in II, one could always simply prove a step inserted as an axiom of I. (Why?) Our demonstration will then consist in showing how to turn proofs in II into quasi-proofs in II in such a way that, when all subordinate proofs are eliminated, the result can be turned into a proof in I. This reduction procedure will begin with the **innermost** proof (that is, one with no proofs subordinate to it). Instructions for eliminating such proofs can then be reapplied to innermost subordinate proofs in the quasi-proofs which result, and so on, until all subordinate proofs are eliminated.

In order to carry through our demonstration, we shall require a method of proof called **mathematical induction**. (This term should not be confused with our earlier use of "induction." Arguments using mathematical induction purport to be *deductive* arguments.) One form of this kind of argument consists first in directing attention to some number n, such as the number of steps in a proof or the number of symbols in a wff. Proving a theorem about *all* wff's or *all* proofs, then, will consist in showing the following two things:

(i) the theorem holds where $n = 1$.
(ii) if the theorem holds where $n < k$, then it holds for k.

The first step is called the **basis** and the second the **inductive** step. The reader should be able to convince himself informally that proving (i) and (ii) together does amount to proving the theorem for all n. In proving (ii), since it is a conditional proposition, we shall be able to *assume* the antecedent and derive the consequent, much as in a CI proof. We shall often refer to this **inductive assumption** when proving the inductive step.

We now proceed to give instructions for successively eliminating innermost proofs in II until the result is a quasi-proof without subordinate proofs. There will be two cases: either (i) the innermost subordinate proof is an NI proof, or (ii) the innermost subordinate proof is a CI proof.

(i) Let Q be an NI proof and the innermost subordinate proof of a proof or quasi-proof P in II. Where the steps of Q are $p_1, p_2, \ldots, p_n$ (we put subscripts on our metavariables for convenience), let Q′ be $Cp_1p_1, Cp_1p_2, \ldots, Cp_1p_n$, and let P′ be the result of replacing the subordinate proof Q in P by the sequence of wff's Q′.

We show by induction on the number of steps n in Q that P′ is convertible into a quasi-proof in II.

Basis. If Q consists of only one step, p_1, then Q′ will consist of the single step Cp_1p_1. It can then be justified in P′ as an instance of the axiom schema A1.

Induction. Assume that the theorem holds for steps $p_{i<k}$ in Q, that is, that P′ to that point is convertible into a quasi-proof in II. We must now show that P′ remains a quasi-proof when Cp_1p_k is added to it. Step p_k may have been justified in Q by (a) borrowing, (b) CE, (c) NNE, or (d) DR. (Why are these the only possibilities?)

(a) If p_k is by borrowing, there is another step p_k in the same proof as the sequence Q′ or borrowable into it. Cp_1p_k is then derivable in P′ by writing down in the outermost proof the appropriate instance of axiom schema A2, $CpCqp$, borrowing it if necessary, and using CE.

(b) If p_k is by CE from steps p_i and Cp_ip_k, then, by the inductive assumption, there are in P′ steps Cp_1p_i and $Cp_1Cp_ip_k$. Cp_1p_k is then derivable in P′ by writing down in the outermost proof the appropriate instance of the axiom schema A3, $CCpqCCpCqrCpr$, borrowing it if necessary, and using CE twice.

(c) If p_k is by NNE from some step NNp_k, then, by the inductive assumption, there is in P′ a step Cp_1NNp_k. Cp_1p_k is then derivable in P′ by writing down in the outermost proof the appropriate instance of axiom schema A4, $CCpNNqCpq$, borrowing it if necessary, and using CE.

(d) If p_k is by DR from some step p_i, then, by the inductive assumption, there is in P′ a step Cp_1p_i. Cp_1p_k is then derivable from Cp_1p_i by DR.

Finally, the step Np_1, which in P was a consequence of the whole NI proof Q, may in P′ be justified since, by the inductive assumption, there are already in P' steps Cp_1p_i and Cp_1Np_i; we may thus write down in the outermost proof the appropriate version of axiom schema A5, $CCpqCCpNqNp$, borrow if necessary, and derive Np_1 by two uses of CE.

(ii) Let Q be a CI proof and the innermost subordinate proof of a proof or quasi-proof P in II. Where the steps of Q are $p_1, p_2, \ldots, p_n$, let Q' be $Cp_1p_1, Cp_1p_2, \ldots, Cp_1p_n$, and let P' be the result of replacing the subordinate proof Q in P by the sequence of wff's Q'. The reader may construct an inductive proof that P' is convertible into a quasi-proof in II in a way precisely analogous to case (i), except that here the step which in P was justified by the whole CI proof will in P' have an identical predecessor by the inductive assumption (why?) and may therefore be justified in the way that its predecessor was.

Repeated application of the instructions embodied in this proof will enable us finally to eliminate all subordinate proofs and thus all uses of NI and CI from quasi-proofs. (This provides us with something like a proof strategy for I *via* proofs in II, although the resulting proofs in I are excessively long and complicated.) Moreover, since in P all uses of B were to justify steps in subordinate proofs, we shall be able to eliminate all uses of this rule. P'', then, the quasi-proof which results when all subordinate proofs have been eliminated, will consist of axioms of I and steps derived by CE, NNE, and DR. Any step derivable by NNE will be derivable by writing down an instance of A4 of the form $CCNNpNNpCNNpp$ and an instance of A1 of the form $CNNpNNp$ and applying CE twice. Then all uses of CE are eliminable in favor of R1 and all uses of DR in favor of R2, and the result is a proof in I. Since we have shown in general how to take any proof in II and turn it into a proof in I, it follows that anything provable in II is provable in I, and our sketch of a proof of the equivalence of I and II is complete.

8.3 We may now prove something about I by way of II and *vice versa*. In dealing with the consistency of the system, it will be most convenient to consider I.

We have described consistency provisionally in terms of the system having only ttt's as theorems. This is, of course, not a general definition, for it would not apply to systems purporting to go beyond propositional logic and having as theorems wff's which are not ttt's. A more adequate definition of consistency, applicable to any system which at least contains negation, is as follows: a system is consistent if and only if no two formulas of the forms p and Np are provable in it. In the case of our current system, this will *follow* if we can show that all our theorems are ttt's. (Why?) To show this, it will suffice to show that all the axioms are ttt's and that the rules when applied to ttt's yield only ttt's.

As for the first question, we leave to the reader the relatively simple but somewhat tedious task of confirming by truth table calculation that all the axioms provided by schemata A1—A5 of I are ttt's. Here it is essential that calculation of truth-values under a given schema amounts to calculation of the truth-values for all the axioms given by that schema. (The reader is left to convince himself that this is so.)

As for the second, consider R1. If p and Cpq are both ttt's, elementary truth table considerations will show that q is also. These conditions on p and Cpq may be represented thus:

$$
\begin{array}{cc}
p & \mathrm{C}\,p\,q \\
t & t \\
t & t \\
t & t \\
. & . \\
. & . \\
. & .
\end{array}
$$

But now we must fill in "t's" under p in Cpq and, to retain the "t's" under the "C," we must put all "t's" under q:

$$
\begin{array}{c}
\mathrm{C}\,p\,q \\
t\ t\ t \\
t\ t\ t \\
t\ t\ t \\
.\ .\ . \\
.\ .\ . \\
.\ .\ .
\end{array}
$$

With regard to R2, since it involves replacing a wff with another wff having the same truth table, the calculation of the value of the ttt to which it is applied will not be affected once we get to the main constant of the substituted wff, or outside it.

Since all the axioms are ttt's and the rules applied to ttt's yield only ttt's, all the theorems of I are ttt's and hence I is consistent, as is II. (What has just been done is in effect a proof by induction on the number of steps, n, in a proof in I that any step in a proof in I is a ttt.

The reader may wish to work out the proof more explicitly in inductive form.)

8.4 We now turn to the proof that our system is *complete*, that it contains all the theorems we want it to contain.[4] In the present case, what we have to show, then, is that all ttt's are provable. Of course, we cannot do this by actually proving all of them, since there are an infinite number. What we must do, then, is provide a procedure whereby it will be possible to construct a proof of any arbitrarily selected ttt. In order to do this, it will be most convenient to consider the System II.

First we show that any wff may be associated with one or more *equivalent* wff's, any one of which is called a **conjunctive normal form** (**cnf**) of the wff. A cnf is a wff (i) containing only proposition stand-ins, "N," "A," and "K," (ii) such that "N" occurs only immediately preceding proposition stand-ins, and (iii) such that all the "K's" are together at the beginning of the wff and all the "A's" either are the main connectives of wff's *joined* by "K" or immediately follow other "A's." (We must also allow for the case where there are no "K's," in which case all the "A's" must be together at the beginning of the wff.) We may discover a cnf of a wff by first eliminating connectives other than the ones mentioned in (i) in favor of their definitional equivalents and then appealing to the following equivalences:

(23) EANpNqNKpq
(24) EKNpNqNApq
(25) EpNNp
(29) EApqAqp
(31) EApKqrKApqApr
(34) EKpKqrKKpqr
(35) EApAqrAApqr

Informally stated, the process of discovering a cnf of a wff may be summarized as follows: after having eliminated "C's" and "E's" to satisfy clause (i), substitute equivalents according to theorems (23) and (24) in such a way as eventually to get all the "N's" applying to proposition stand-ins or to other "N's". Then substitute according to

---

[4] The strategy for this completeness proof is fundamentally that of Hilbert and Ackermann [20], pp. 30–38, 42–43.

(25) to eliminate extra "N's" and get an expression satisfying clause (ii). In order to satisfy clause (iii), substitute according to (29), if necessary, in order to substitute according to (31). This sort of maneuver will eventually make all the "A's" apply to propositional variables or to other "A's" and will make all the "K's" apply to "A's" to which other "A's" do not apply, or to other "K's." Then, if necessary, substitute according to (34) and (35) in order to get the "K's" and "A's" grouped as specified in clause (iii).

Still proceeding informally, and substituting equivalent expressions for one another, we may see how this works in the case of the following wff, which happens also to be a ttt.

(i) CKCpqNqNp

First, we eliminate the "C's":

(ii) ANKANpqNqNp

We now use (23) to drive the first "N" in part way:

(iii) AANANpqNNqNp

Next (24) enables us to drive it in all the way:

(iv) AAKNNpNqNNqNp

Now (25) enables us to dispense with the double "N's":

(v) AAKpNqqNp

We must now get the "K" to the outside. In order to do this, we must first use (29):

(vi) AAqKpNqNp

Now we can use (31):

(vii) AKAqpAqNqNp

Next we must use (29) again:

(viii) ANpKAqpAqNq

Another use of (31) yields:

(ix) KANpAqpANpAqNq

Finally, applications of (35) yield a formula of the required sort:

(x) KAANpqpAANpqNq

In order to apply these insights to our system, it will first be necessary to derive in II a rule, reminiscent of DR, which states that whenever we have a step p containing some (proper or improper) part which is a wff q and we also have Eqr (or Erq), we may write down another wff s which is just like p except that it contains r in place of q.

We may derive this rule by considering the forms p might take. First, where p is q (that is, where q is an improper part of p), then s is r, and the desired result follows directly by EE. Now we must show that the rule holds if p is of the forms (i) Nq, (ii) Cqt, or (iii) Ctq; then we shall be able to show that the rule holds for more complicated cases as well and thus, since "C" and "N" are the only connectives we need consider, for all cases.

(i) if p is of the form Nq, then s will be of the form Nr. The derivation for the case where we have Eqr follows. (In this and the following cases, the proof would be similar where we had Erq.)

.	.	.
.	.	.
l	Nq	Ri
.	.	.
.	.	.
m	Eqr	Rj
.	.	.
.	.	.
n	r	HP(NI)
$n+1$	Eqr	B, m
$n+2$	q	EE, $n+1$, n
$n+3$	Nq	B, l
$n+4$	Nr	NI, n—$(n+3)[n+2, n+3]$
.	.	.
.	.	.

(ii) if p is of the form Cqt, then s will be of the form Crt. The derivation follows:

.	.	.
.	.	.
l	Cqt	Ri
.	.	.
.	.	.
m	Eqr	Rj
.	.	.
.	.	.
n	r	HP(CI)
$n+1$	Eqr	B, m
$n+2$	q	EE, n, $n+1$
$n+3$	Cqt	B, l
$n+4$	t	CE, $n+2$, $n+3$
$n+5$	Crt	CI, n—($n+4$)
.	.	.
.	.	.

(iii) if p is of the form Ctq, then s will be of the form Ctr. The derivation is similar to that of case (ii) above and is left to the reader.

Now, however, we have derived the rule for all cases, for if the wff is more complex than proposition stand-ins immediately joined by connectives and the substitution takes place *within* one of the constituent wff's, it will be possible to show in successive stages that the wff's immediately joined by the main connective are equivalent. Thus, for example, if we wanted to use our rule to move in some proof from "NCpNNr" to "NCpr," given that we have "ENNrr," we must first derive "ECpNNrCpr," appealing to case (iii), and then appeal to case (i) to derive the desired result:

.	.	.
.	.	.
l	NCpNNr	Ri
.	.	.

m	ENNrr	Rj
·	·	·
·	·	·
·	·	·
n	CpNNr	HP(EI)
$n+1$	ENNrr	B, m
$n+2$	Cpr	Case (iii), n, $n+1$
$n+3$	Cpr	HP(EI)
$n+4$	ENNrr	B, m
$n+5$	CpNNr	Case (iii), $n+3$, $n+4$
$n+6$	ECpNNrCpr	EI, n—$(n+2)$, $(n+3)$—$(n+5)$
$n+7$	NCpr	Case (i), l, $n+6$
·	·	·
·	·	·

Similarly we may apply the rule to any more complex wff employing only "N" and "C." Since all our wff's may be thus expressed, we can apply the rule to any wff, which is what we wanted to show.

What all this means in terms of System II is that it is possible to move in that system from a wff to its cnf by way of proof of appropriate forms of theorems (23), (24), (25), (29), (31), (34), and (35), and uses of the rule of substituting equivalences just derived. Since formulas (i)—(x) are all equivalent, it will be equally possible to move from the cnf to the original wff in the same way.

Returning to our cnf, recall that our sample calculation began with a ttt. Now notice a peculiar feature of (x) above. Each of the expressions to which a "K" applies is a series of "A's" followed by proposition stand-ins or negated proposition stand-ins. So much is true of any cnf. But in each of these strings of stand-ins and negates of stand-ins will be found some proposition stand-in together with *its* negate. Elementary truth table considerations will show that, for all (and only) cnf's which purport to be equivalent to ttt's and which must hence themselves be ttt's, each such string of proposition stand-ins and their negates must thus contain some proposition stand-in together with its negate.

Turning again to System II, we can see that, *if* we can provide a proof of the cnf of a wff, we can provide a proof of the wff as outlined above. Given the condition which a cnf must meet to be a cnf of a ttt, it is easy to construct such a proof of a cnf of any ttt and then, in the way outlined above, a proof of the ttt. One must only prove the appropriate counterpart of

(3) ApNp,

use AI to tack on other necessary proposition stand-ins or their negates, appeal to (35), (29), and our derived rule if needed to get everything in the right order, and, after having thus constructed each of the component wff's consisting of a string of "A's" followed by proposition stand-ins or their negates, stick them all together in the appropriate order using KI.

We now have general directions for constructing a proof in II of any arbitrarily selected ttt by means of a proof of its cnf in the manner just described and then a derivation of the ttt from the cnf by a process whose broad outlines approximate (i)—(x) reversed. Of course, this would not always give us the neatest or the most obvious proof; in fact, a proof constructed on these lines of the theorem just considered would be very long indeed, especially if the derived rule involving substitution of equivalences were not allowed. (The reader is invited but not urged, or even recommended, to construct it.) For present purposes, however, these directions provide what no collection of proofs could ever provide, a completely general description, specifiable on demand, of how to discover a proof for any arbitrarily selected ttt, and this amounts to a proof that System II (and hence System I as well) is complete.

8.5 In discussing consistency and completeness, some of our accounts of these properties have stressed the relation of our system to some preselected set of wff's which it was intended to generate as theorems. But it is not always as easy to specify the theorems independent of the deductive system and then consider the system in relation to the set of theorems thus specified. Because of this, there have been attempts to give accounts of the notions of consistency and completeness in such a way that they can be understood and applied merely by dealing with the system itself.

Completeness has thus been defined as the property a system has if the addition to it of a wff which is not a theorem results in a contradiction being derivable in the system. In the present case, though not necessarily in other cases, completeness in this sense, often called **absolute completeness**, may be seen to amount to the same thing as completeness in our earlier sense, often called **relative completeness**, at least to the extent that our system can be shown to be relatively complete if and only if it is absolutely complete.

(i) If the system is relatively complete, it is absolutely complete, for consider the result of taking as provable a wff which is not a theorem in the relatively complete system. This new "theorem" will not be a ttt and hence its cnf will not be of the specified form. If the "theorem" is provable, however, so is the cnf, and from the cnf a contradiction may be derived as follows. Prove the "theorem" and hence the cnf in such a form that a part of the cnf *not* containing a proposition stand-in together with its negate consists of "A's" followed only by occurrences of the *same* proposition stand-ins. (To discover what version of the "theorem" will yield this cnf, substitute in it some proposition stand-in, say "p," for each unnegated proposition stand-in in the part of the cnf in question and "Np" for each negated proposition stand-in in that part of the cnf. This can be done if and only if the cnf is not a ttt. Why?) But then successive applications of KE will yield the part of the cnf in question alone and appeal to appropriate versions of theorem (22) "EAppp," the substitution rule just derived, and EE will eventually yield the proposition stand-in "p" alone. The same process will, however, yield the negation of that proposition stand-in "Np" if we prove the "theorem" in the form as above except that "Np" is substituted where "p" was before, and "p" where "Np" was.

(ii) If the system is absolutely complete, it is relatively complete, for consider if the system were not relatively complete. Then there would be some ttt not provable. But if this ttt were taken as provable in the system, no contradiction would follow and thus the system would not have been absolutely complete, for applying our rules (considering now system I) to ttt's yields only other ttt's, as we have already shown in our proof of relative consistency, and hence no two formulas of the forms p and Np.

Our notion of consistency, unlike that of completeness, has already been stated in such a way that it can be understood without reference to the relation of the system to some already specified set of theorems. This disparity may be traced to the fact that the very word "completeness" seems to carry at least a prima facie suggestion of relatedness which is absent from "consistency." That is, an "absolute" definition of completeness such as we have just given seems at first to lack intuitive content, whereas it would be a "relative" definition of consistency of which this could be said. In the present case, however, we can show that our system is consistent if and only if all the theorems are ttt's. (The proof of this fact, the material for which has already been provided, will be left to the reader.) Informally, then, just as our system is said to be relatively complete if it has *all* the desired theorems, it may be said to be "relatively" consistent if it has *only* the desired theorems.

The fact that we were able to find a property specifiable purely "formally" which held if and only if the system was relatively complete provides some grounds for hope that we can deal with the question of completeness even when, as often happens, there is no such readily specifiable aim as having all ttt's as theorems. Even though, however, we did not *define* consistency with respect to a given set of already specified theorems, we did *prove* it by appealing to the fact that all the theorems were ttt's. Thus it has seemed important to try to discover, if not a definition, at least a *criterion* of consistency which can not only be stated but applied to a system without reference to some previously specified set of theorems it is intended to embody. It has thus been proposed that a system is consistent if there is at least one wff which is not a theorem.[5] (This criterion, unlike our earlier definition, applies even to systems which lack negation.) The plausibility of this proposed criterion may be seen by reflecting on the principles embodied in our derived rule of NE, which may be thought of as claiming that anything is provable if a contradiction is provable. Thus, if there is something not provable, no contradiction is provable.

Although our system can most easily be shown consistent on this criterion by appealing to the fact that, since only ttt's are provable, "p" for example is not, we at least now have the possibility of demonstrating consistency simply by showing that there is no proof of a given wff, without appealing to some independent characterization of the theorems. (Of course this demonstration will not consist simply in failing to find a proof.)

---

[5] This criterion of consistency is often called the Post criterion, after the logician E. L. Post, although it is not, in fact, the criterion he proposed.

9

Modalities

9.1 If logic is the study of entailment, and entailments are representable by logically true "if . . . then" propositions, it is not surprising that some of the major controversies in logic have centered around the notion "if . . . then" and the relationship we have symbolized by "C." We have already seen, for example, that according to the truth table for "C" and the view that "C" represents "if . . . then," the proposition "If the moon is made of green cheese, then George Washington was the first President of the United States" is true. This may seem a bit difficult to accept, and, as we have seen, it has been taken as evidence that "C" does not adequately represent "if . . . then." (Recalling our claim that it is surely the nearest truth-functional approximation, we may say that the contention ultimately is that "if . . . then" is not truth-functional.) Whatever the state of this question, it should be clear that to say that this proposition is true is not to say that there is a valid argument from its antecedent to its consequent; this claim is made only when the "if . . . then" proposition is said to be *logically* true, only when, in terms of our system, there is a *theorem* beginning with "C" which represents its form.

Even here, however, there are problems. We have seen theorems which have seemed questionable to the extent that they claim to show certain modes of inference to be valid, among which the following may be taken as representative:

$$(9) \ CNpCpq \qquad -p \to p \to q$$
$$(11) \ CqCpq \qquad q \to p \to q$$

These theorems have been called **paradoxes of material implication,** "material implication" being a name often given to the relationship we have symbolized by "C." We have already discussed some of the difficulties with (11) in 5.8, but we have not considered the supposed features of it which led philosophers to regard it as paradoxical. These theorems were thought to be paradoxical as involving commitment to the views that anything whatsoever follows from a false proposition and that a true proposition follows from anything whatsoever. Now these would seem to be false statements about the relation of entailment which we set out to capture formally. The "paradox" of the theorems, then, would be simply that entailments which are certified by them do not hold and the system is to that extent inadequate. But do these theorems certify the entailments they are thought to certify?

Let us look more closely at (9), which is supposed to involve the claim that anything follows from a false proposition. It may help to state this claim more fully:

(i) It follows from a proposition's being false that any proposition whatsoever follows from that proposition.

The "anything" part should be clear; "q" could be a stand-in for any proposition whatsoever, without regard to any lack of relationship between that proposition and the one for which "p" is a stand-in. (Our example in 5.8 was chosen to demonstrate a case where the lack of apparent relationship was dramatically evident.) But the difficulty with regarding (9) as involving this claim should also be apparent; it is, quite simply, that we are regarding *both* "C's" as representing entailments, whereas only the first is supposed to. If we observe this hidden distinction between the two occurrences of "C" in (9), it appears that all we are committed to is something like the following:

(ii) It follows from a proposition's being false that any "if . . . then" proposition having that false proposition as an antecedent is true.

This claim, which is closer to what we discussed in 5.8, involves difficulties of its own, but, if it is false, it is not false for the same reasons as (i). It depends primarily on the truth-functional interpretation of "if . . . then" propositions in general. One can accept that interpretation, and with it (ii), without being committed to the obviously false (i).

It is important to see that (i) and (ii) are not what we might call proposed **readings** of the theorems but rather statements of what acceptance of the theorems is supposed to commit us to. The difference between these two things is that in the former the proposition stand-ins would be *used*, while in the latter they would not. (For example, in both cases (i) and (ii) we stated the first part of the claim as "It follows from a proposition's being false . . ." rather than something like "If it is not the case that p . . . .") We could equally well discover two possible readings of (9). In order to do this, we shall require a notion which stands to "follows from" or "entails" as, for example, "it is not the case that" stands to "is false." "If . . . then" will not do, of course, for this has been preempted by a relationship ("C") which we have stressed holds in many cases where entailment does not. In view of the connection, if not identity, between "if . . . then" and entailment, however, and also in view of the historical use of the term "necessary" to describe the status of logical truths, we adopt "necessarily [if . . . then]," where "necessarily" applies to the whole "if . . . then" proposition, as indicated by the brackets (or by parentheses). The alternative readings of the theorem would then be as follows:

    (iii) Corresponding to (i), "Necessarily [if it's not the case that p, then necessarily (if p, then q)]."

    (iv) Corresponding to (ii), "Necessarily [if it's not the case that p, then (if p, then q)]."

In these readings, of course, the obviously invalid form (iii) is just as obviously not a correct reading of (9), while the correct reading given in (iv) is not such an obviously invalid form, or at least is not invalid for the same reasons. Apparently the only way we would be tempted to think of (9) as involving a commitment to (i) would be if we looked at a careless reading of (9), something like

    (v) If it's not the case that p, then if p, then q

(a reading which does not preserve the distinction between the two occurrences of "C") and then, dimly sensing that the first "C" involves an entailment claim but not distinguishing the two occurrences of "C," we interpreted (v) as involving the claim embodied in (i).

Nonetheless, it does appear that there are differences of significance among different occurrences of "C," and this fact encourages these misunderstandings, besides being, on the face of it, bad practice in the use of symbols. If our concern is with entailment, the project therefore suggests itself of trying to develop in a formal system a relationship which holds if and only if there is an entailment present (which is not true, of course, of the "C.") If we accept much of what has been said so far in this book, however, we have an immediate clue where to look for such a relationship; it will hold whenever the "C" represents not just a true "if . . . then" propositions but a logically true "if . . . then" proposition.

In order to systematize this notion, we shall have to develop the basic idea of **necessity** and related **modal** notions which can be defined in terms of it. We shall thus have to introduce new logical connectives into our system, or, since most of them will be like "N" in not so much connecting two things as applying to one, new **logical constants**, a term which we may regard as applying also to what we have hitherto called "connectives." "Necessity" here refers to a property which logically true propositions have, not to any notions such as might be involved in propositions such as "It is necessary for you to come at once" or "If a body is dropped, it will necessarily fall." These constants will not be truth-functional, as a little reflection should show. Adopting an obvious formation rule, the only remotely plausible truth table for "necessarily p" is as follows:

necessarily p	
t	t
f	f

Adopting this as a definition of necessity, however, would result immediately in the breakdown of the distinction between factual and necessary truths which is precisely what is essential at the moment. All true propositions would be necessarily true.

To the study of these non-truth-functional modal notions we now turn. We shall refer to the system developed in this chapter as the **modal propositional calculus.**[1]

9.2   From now on we shall develop our systems only by means of natural deduction rules, since decision procedures are not always available, and natural deduction rules are more easily motivated than axioms and the discovery of proofs easier in natural deduction systems. The methatheoretic questions often more easily answered if the system is developed axiomatically will not be dealt with in the development of further systems in this chapter and in Chapter 11.

In order to develop the modal propositional calculus, then, we

---

[1] The classic source for the study of systems of modal logic is Lewis and Langford [23]. The part dealing with modal logic is due to Lewis. The system is developed axiomatically on pp. 122ff. The interpretation of the system and its import for the study of deducibility are discussed in Ch. VIII. Selections from this book appear in Iseminger [21]. There have also been attempts to deal with modal notions in systems analogous to truth-functional systems except that more than the two values "t" and "f" may be assumed by proposition stand-ins. Lewis argues that these systems cannot succeed in capturing modal notions (Ch. VII.) Nonetheless, they are interesting in their own right. See Prior [34], pp. 230–250.

shall take System II in 8 and first add the symbol "L," to be read "necessarily" and to apply to the wff immediately following. Our next job is to specify rules of LI and LE.

The rule of necessity elimination (LE) is intuitively fairly obvious and not difficult to formulate. Necessarily true propositions are, a fortiori, true. Schematically this means we can drop "L's" at the beginnings of wffs at will, thus:

$$(LE) \quad \begin{array}{c|c|c} \cdot & \cdot & \cdot \\ \cdot & \cdot & \cdot \\ m & Lp & Ri \\ \cdot & \cdot & \\ \cdot & \cdot & \cdot \\ n & p & LE,\ m \\ \cdot & \cdot & \cdot \\ \cdot & \cdot & \end{array}$$

This rule will prove useful when using the rules already available in the propositional calculus, since in general it will only be possible to apply essential elimination rules after the "L" has been dropped.

The rule of LI is somewhat more complicated. We obviously do not want to be able to tack on "L's" indiscriminately, since this would lead immediately to the provability of "EpLp" and the consequent breakdown of the distinction between necessary truths and others. (Why?) It would be tantamount to giving the truth table definition of "L" rejected in 9.1. The leading idea of our method of deriving a formula Lp is this: a proposition can be asserted necessarily only when it is derivable from other propositions asserted necessarily. A proposition is logically true if and only if it is deducible from other logical truths. (The reader should reflect on this principle; we do not stop to justify it here.) To schematize this rule, we need a means of making it clear when we have derived a wff only from wff's representing forms of logical truths. We can achieve this by introducing a new kind of subordinate proof (i) having no hypothesis and (ii) such that only propositions of the form Lp can be borrowed into it or past it into proofs subordinate to it. We signify such a proof by putting an "L" immediately to the left of where its vertical line begins and specify that any wff which can be got inside such a proof (to be called a **strict subordinate proof**) can be written down, below the strict subordinate proof and with an "L" prefixed, in the proof to which the strict proof is immediately subordinate.

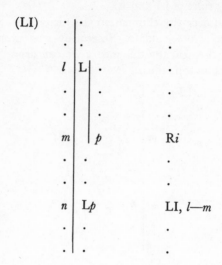

We may now prove some theorems in the modal propositional calculus.

First, it is worth noting that our rules permit us to write down immediately any theorem in the propositional calculus with an "L" prefixed to it. This can be accomplished simply by carrying out a proof of the theorem inside a strict subordinate proof and then moving it out and prefixing an "L." Consider, for example,

(2) Cpp.

We can readily prove

(37) LCpp

as follows:

$$
\begin{array}{lll}
(37) & 1\ |L|\ \ |{\rule[-0.6ex]{0.4pt}{1.6ex}}p & \text{HP(CI)} \\
& 2\ |\ \ \ |\ \text{Cpp} & \text{CI, } 1\text{—}1 \\
& 3\ |\ \text{LCpp} & \text{LI, } 1\text{—}2 \\
\end{array}
$$

(Note that in this proof the LI proof 1—2 is without hypotheses in the required sense; step 1 is a hypothesis of the CI proof.) That we can carry out such a proof with any of the theorems in the propositional calculus should not surprise us if we recall that part of our original intention was that all our theorems should represent forms of logically true propositions.

The following proofs will illustrate the use of these rules. The only new strategy involved is this: do not use LE until necessary, since what it is applied to will be borrowable into a strict proof while what results from its application will not generally be borrowable into such a proof. Withholding the use of LE until necessary thus enables one to retain a certain flexibility of operation.

(38)	1	KLpLq	HP(CI)
	2	Lp	KE, 1
	3	Lq	KE, 1
	4	L Lp	B, 2
	5	Lq	B, 3
	6	p	LE, 4
	7	q	LE, 5
	8	Kpq	KI, 6, 7
	9	LKpq	LI, 4—8
	10	CKLpLqLKpq	CI, 1—9

(39)	1	ALpLq	HP(CI)
	2	Lp	HP(AE)
	3	L Lp	B, 2
	4	p	LE, 3
	5	Apq	AI, 4
	6	LApq	LI, 3—5
	7	Lq	HP(AE)
	8	L Lq	B, 7
	9	q	LE, 8
	10	Apq	AI, 9
	11	LApq	LI, 8—10
	12	LApq	AE, 1, 2—6, 7—11
	13	CALpLqLApq	CI, 1—12

The converse of (38),

(40) CLKpqKLpLq,

and hence the following equivalence,

(41) ELKpqKLpLq,

are provable. These proofs are left to the reader. The converse of (39) is not a theorem. The reader should both convince himself intuitively that it should not be and see where an attempted proof breaks down. (This would not be to prove that it is not a theorem, of course.)

9.3 It is now possible to introduce further defined modalities and derive I and E rules for them in much the same way as we did in the propositional calculus, except that here we shall derive some of the rules as we introduce them.

The constant "M," to be read "possibly" and having the same kind of formation rule as "L," is introduced in the following definition:

D4. Mp and NLNp are equivalent by definition.

The notion of possibility involved here, of course, is simply that which applies to any proposition which is not self-contradictory (whose denial is not logically necessary, to interpret the definition.) In this sense of "possible," propositions like "The moon is made of green cheese" are possible, while "Brutus killed Caesar and it's not the case that Brutus killed Caesar" is not. To be possible in this sense is evidently a very minor achievement for a proposition, considerably less than being "plausible" or "reasonable," and certainly less than being true.

The introduction rule for "M," then, is obvious, if anything true is a fortiori possible.

(MI)

m	p	Ri
n	Mp	MI, m

The derivation of this rule, using "L" and "N" rules plus B, DR, and hypotheses as permitted, is left to the reader.

The rule ME is less obvious. It says, in effect, that, given the possibility of p and the derivation of q from p, we can assert the possibility of q. Schematically:

(ME)

k	Mp	Ri
l	L$\mid p$	HP(ME)
m	q	Rj
n	Mq	ME, k, l—m

Notice that this rule appears to involve a subordinate proof which both is strict and has a hypothesis. The following derivation will show that the hypothesis is really that of a CI proof which is subordinate to a strict LI proof. It is convenient here and in some of the rules which follow to superimpose, as it were, the CI proof on the strict proof to which it is subordinate and to write the hypothesis as if it were a hypothesis of that strict proof.

(ME)

	·	·	·
	·	·	·
k	Mp		Ri
	·	·	·
	·	·	·
l	NLNp		DR, k (D4)
	·	·	·
	·	·	·
m	LNq		HP(NI)
$m + 1$	L	p	HP(CI)
	·	·	·
	·	·	·
	·	·	·
n		q	Rj
$n + 1$		Cpq	CI, $(m + 1)$—n
$n + 2$		LNq	B, m
$n + 3$		Nq	LE, $n + 2$
$n + 4$		Np	MT (derived rule), $n + 1$, $n + 3$
$n + 5$		LNp	LI, $(m + 1)$—$(n + 4)$
$n + 6$		NLNp	B, l
$n + 7$	NLNq		NI, m—$(n + 6)$[$n + 5$, $n + 6$]
$n + 8$	Mq		DR, $n + 7$ (D4)
	·	·	·
	·	·	·

We shall merely list a couple of theorems whose proofs employ these rules, since our main concern is not with this particular modal notion.[2]

---

[2] Lewis takes as his primitive notion the notion we have symbolized as "M," defining others, including the one we are mainly interested in, in terms of it. See [23], p. 124, although our notion of possibility and Lewis's are not identical.

(42) CAMpMqMApq
(43) CMApqAMpMq
(44) CMKpqKMpMq

Theorem (43) can be proved by first proving a theorem of the same form as theorem (1), namely

AMpNMp,

and then using AE. The converse of (44) is not a theorem.

9.4 The definition of the constant we are mainly interested in, which is to symbolize a relationship which holds if and only if an entailment relationship holds, emerges readily from the suggestion that it hold just when the "C" represents a necessarily true "if . . . then." If we make the constant in question "C′," which has a formation rule like that for "C," the definition is as follows:

D5. C′pq and LCpq are equivalent by definition.

It is customary to read formulas of the form C′pq as "p strictly implies q." "Strictly implies," like "implies" and "is false," is a construction which involves mentioning rather than using the propositions to which it is applied. For a reading we would prefer something like "it is not the case that" or "if . . . then," which involve using the propositions joined. "Necessarily if . . . then," which suggested itself earlier, becomes tedious and unwieldy very quickly. Having been duly warned, the reader may adopt the reading "p strictly implies q" as a convenient, if not strictly accurate, means of interpreting the claims in behalf of which theorems involving "C′" may be invoked.

The elimination rule, whose derivation is left to the reader, may be schematized thus: (C′E)

l	C′pq	Ri
m	Lp	Rj
n	Lq	C′E, l, m

Another version, as follows, which is perhaps more useful, is also derivable:

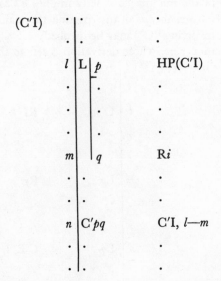

(C'E)

l C'pq Ri

m p Rj

n q C'E, l, m

The introduction rule, which is fairly obvious, may be schematized thus, adopting as with ME in 9.3 the convention of superimposing a CI proof on the strict subordinate proof to which it is immediately subordinate:

(C'I)

l L p HP(C'I)

m q Ri

n C'pq C'I, l—m

The derivation will be left to the reader.

Following is a proof using C′I. It will be convenient (and obviously a mere shortcut enabling us to do nothing new) to permit expressions beginning with "C′" and "NMN" (and "E′" introduced below) to be borrowed directly into strict subordinate proofs. The strategy in C′I proofs will be like that in CI proofs, subject to the restrictions on borrowing introduced by the use of a strict subordinate proof.

(45)   1 | L | C′pq   HP(C′I)

        2 | | L | Nq   HP(C′I)

        3 | | | C′pq   B, 1

        4 | | | LCpq   DR, 3 (D5)

        5 | | | Cpq   LE, 4

        6 | | | Np   MT (derived rule), 2, 5

        7 | | C′NqNp   C′I, 2—6

        8 | C′C′pqC′NqNp   C′I, 1—7

We can represent a relationship which holds between propositions when they entail one another by introducing the symbol "E′," with a formation rule like that for "E," defined in the following way:

D6. E′pq and NCLCpqNLCqp are equivalent by definition.

We shall not here discuss rules of E′I and E′E. (See Appendix C.)

9.5 It would be possible to go on to a point by point comparison of "C" and "C′," listing and proving many more theorems.[3] The aim of this whole enterprise, however, was to discover a constant about which theorems comparable to (9) and (11) were not provable and which would thus be a better candidate to be the formal representation of a relationship which holds if and only if entailment or deducibility holds. We shall, therefore, turn directly to this and related questions with regard to "C′" and (9). The reader should ask similar questions with respect to (11). (It is again to be emphasized that we will not here prove that any wff's are not theorems.)

[3] The system presented here is equivalent to Lewis's S4. The various systems Lewis discusses are distinguished mainly by the ways in which they deal with iterated modalities. See [23], pp. 500ff. In the present system "E′LpLLp" is provable. (How?) It is worth reflecting whether we want such a theorem.

The wff corresponding to (9) which we do not want provable on pain of being committed to the view that anything follows from a false proposition is

(i) C'NpC'pq.

The attempt to prove it would proceed as follows:

1	L⌐Np	HP(C'I)
2	L⌐p	HP(C'I)
.	.	.
.	.	.
.	.	.
n	q	?
$n+1$	C'pq	C'I, 2—n
$n+2$	C'NpC'pq	C'I, 1—($n+1$)

It is clear that the only way we could do anything in the innermost subordinate proof is by borrowing in step 1, but we are prevented from doing this by the restrictions imposed on borrowing into strict subordinate proofs.

There are a number of theorems which remain provable, however, and we must convince ourselves that they are not "paradoxical" in the present sense if we are to regard the system as fulfilling its purposes. For one thing, (9) remains as provable as ever. (Why should this not bother us?) So, too, on the principle that we can prefix an "L" to any theorem, does

(46) C'NpCpq.

(Why should this not bother us?)

With a final set of theorems, however, we cannot be so cavalier. The reason we were unable to complete the proof of (i), the restriction on borrowing, immediately suggests a related principle which is provable and whose proof is left to the reader,

(47) C'LNpC'pq.

This theorem evidently commits us to saying, not that anything follows from a false proposition, but that anything follows from a necessarily false proposition. Another theorem which commits us to something like the same thing, if a self-contradiction is taken to be the prototype of a necessarily false proposition, is

(48) C'KpNpq.

This theorem is readily proved using only underived rules, but the following derivation using MTP illustrates most graphically how the principle embodied in this theorem is reducible to a very few apparently quite plausible rules.

(48)   1 | L | KpNp   HP(C'I)

          2 | | p   KE, 1

          3 | | Apq   AI, 2

          4 | | Np   KE, 1

          5 | | q   MTP (derived rule), 3, 4

          6 | C'KpNpq   C'I, 1—5

These theorems and others like them have been called **paradoxes of strict implication**. Needless to say, the proponents of strict implication have tried to argue that the theorems are not paradoxical in the present sense, that the entailments which these theorems lead us to think hold do hold. It is certainly true that impugning the validity of the principle involved in (48) must entail impugning the validity of one of the principles expressed by the rules used to derive it, and it is not easy to see which of those one would dispense with in preference to keeping the theorem.[4]

What is it that makes the theorem seem to be paradoxical in the present sense? No doubt it is a part of what seems to be involved in the notion of entailment which we have barely hinted at, the idea that if one proposition follows from another they must have something to do with one another, there must be some **relationship of meaning** between them. Any assertion that any proposition whatsoever follows from a given proposition seems bound to clash with this idea, for it

---

[4] Lewis's argument that the paradoxes are "unavoidable consequences of indispensable rules of inference" (p. 512) amounts to our derivation of theorem (48). See Anderson and Belnap in Iseminger [21] for an attempt to dispense with some of these rules.

seems unlikely that there is any proposition which has such a relationship of meaning to any other proposition whatsoever. Another factor in making the claim that anything follows from a necessarily false proposition seem false, and the theorems embodying that claim therefore seem paradoxical, may be the feeling that somehow, if we can once assert a necessarily false proposition, this principle will enable us to get away with murder. Any doubts of this sort can, however, be resolved by noting that by definition the stated condition can never be fulfilled.

We shall not here go more deeply into the attempt to develop formally an entailment relationship which holds only where there is a connection of meaning between the propositions said to stand in this relationship and which thus has no theorems corresponding to (47) and (48).[5] Since except in specifically modal contexts the entailment claims sanctioned by the theorems of the propositional calculus do not differ from those sanctioned by the modal propositional calculus, and since the indiscriminate combination of modal notions with notions to be introduced shortly leads to difficulties,[6] we shall in our further developments simply add new notions to the propositional calculus and see what entailments and equivalences hold among these new notions by proving theorems beginning with "C" and "E."

[5] See Anderson and Belnap [2], reprinted in part and in revised form in Iseminger [21], for an account of one such attempt.

[6] For some of these difficulties see Quine [37], Ch. VIII, and [38], pp. 195–200.

10

Quantifiers

10.1 We have now gone as far as we can in discussing entailments whose validity depends upon logical constants which join or apply to whole propositions. It should be apparent, however, that there are valid deductions whose obvious validity will not yield to the tools of analysis currently available. Consider the following: "If every man is mortal and Socrates is a man, then Socrates is mortal." We could only represent its form by a wff like "CKpqr," which is not, of course, a theorem. It is clear that the logical truth of this proposition depends upon, among other things, the concept "every," the fact that "man" occurs in the first constituent proposition and the second, the fact that "mortal" occurs in the first and the third, and the fact that "Socrates" occurs in the second and the third. To give an account of the logical truth of this proposition and of the validity of the inference it embodies, we shall have to refine our analysis to the point where we can break these constituent simple propositions into their elements, and we shall have to discuss the behavior of logical constants such as "every" and its relatives. In terms of the resources already available, we shall have to add to the propositional calculus new symbols to represent the elements into which we analyze propositions and new constants to represent "every" and "some."

10.2 How shall we analyze a proposition such as "Socrates is a man"? (We begin with this simple proposition without any illusions that all propositions are as readily analyzed; we shall first develop our tools to handle this case and hope that they can be developed and extended to handle more difficult cases.) We can say, to begin with,

107

that it breaks into two parts, roughly analogous to parts which grammarians distinguish when they talk of subjects and predicates, in one
sense of those terms, a part ("Socrates") which says who or what we
are talking about (Socrates) and a part ("is a man") which says something about what we are talking about (that it is a man.) Let us call
these parts the **name** and the **predicate**, respectively, remembering
that we are referring to elements which logical analysis purports to
discover in propositions, not elements which grammatical analysis
purports to discover in sentence-types.

At this point, "metaphysical" questions such as those which concerned us in our discussion of propositions arise again. We shall only
mention them. On the fairly natural (but debatable[1]) assumption that
the meaning of "Socrates" is the man Socrates and the equally natural
assumption that all the elements of a proposition are meaningful, we
are led to look for something which stands in the same relationship
to "is a man" as Socrates does to "Socrates." Evidently Being a Man
would be such a thing, but what sort of thing is it? We have all seen
men, but have we seen Being a Man? Individual men have histories,
spatio-temporal location, but Being a Man does not seem to, at least
not in the same way. Once again philosophical reflection on problems
in logic leads to questions concerning a kind of entity which seems mys-
terious and puzzling. Questions concerning the existence and nature of
such entities, called variously "universals," "properties," and "qual-
ities" (and other names as well, not that they are all equivalent),
have been at the center of philosophical controversy since the time
of Plato, and the procedures of modern logic have both given these
questions new forms and suggested new ways of answering them.[2]

10.3 Let us now begin to enrich our system in order to accommodate this analysis of simple propositions into their constituent parts.

We shall require **variables** to serve as stand-ins for names. These
variables will be like proposition stand-ins in that they can be thought
of as holding places in forms which can be filled in to yield propositions,
but there will soon be other operations which we sanction with these
variables which justify us in giving them this different kind of designation.[3] As **name variables**, then, we employ lower-case letters "x,"
"y," "z," "u," and so on. We shall also require stand-ins for predicates,

bearing precisely the same relationship to predicates that proposition stand-ins bear to propositions. As **predicate stand-ins**, then, we employ the lower-case letters "f," "g," "h," and so on.

Our formation rule, to be added to the formation rules for the propositional calculus, may be given provisionally as follows: a predicate stand-in immediately followed by any number of name variables is a wff. Thus "fx," "gy," "fxyz," "Afxgx," and "gyy" are wff's; "fxgx," "Kxy," "fg," and "xy" are not. The simplest cases, such as "fx," then, would obviously represent the form of simple propositions such as "Socrates is a man," and the propriety of enabling such wff's to be combined, like proposition stand-ins, with the connectives already studied should be obvious, as should be the necessity of having at least one each of predicate stand-ins and name variables and the impropriety of permitting symbols of either kind to stand separately or combined with propositional connectives without being combined with one another.

What kind of interpretation can we give to expressions like "fxy"? This simple expansion of our formation rules to allow wff's where more than a single name variable follows a given occurrence of a predicate stand-in allows us to represent the forms of propositions involving predicates like "is next to," "is taller than," and "gave . . . to," predicates traditionally called **relational predicates**, which must be combined with more than one name to form a proposition. Thus "fxy" represents a form of "Socrates is taller than Plato," and (if "x" and "y" are still replacing "Socrates" and "Plato," respectively) "fyx," by a suitable convention regarding the ordering of name variables after relational predicate stand-ins, represents a form of "Plato is taller than Socrates." Similarly "gxyz" represents a form of "John gave the book to Tom." (Recall here our remarks about "Tom and Jim are cousins" in 5.8.) We shall not study the properties of relational predicates themselves in this work, although some of the questions we ask will require us to consider some contexts in which wff's with more than a single name variable following a given occurrence of a predicate stand-in occur.[4]

---

[4] Among the claims often made in behalf of modern logic are that it has led us to realize the logical importance of relational predicates and thereby clarified many entailments previously untouched by formal logic and that it has avoided confusions which arise when relational predicates and others are not carefully distinguished from one another. See Russell [41], pp. 44ff. For a more formal treatment of relations, see Suppes [46], Ch. 10.

We must now revise our formation rules slightly. Once we have the notion of a predicate requiring more than one name to be joined with it to form a proposition, it should be clear that we want to exclude the possibility of a given predicate requiring simultaneously, say, one and two names. Surely any given predicate must require one, as "is red" appears to, *or* two, as "is taller than" appears to, etc., where the "or" is an exclusive "or." Hence we must exclude formulas, such as "Kfxfxy," which could be the forms only of propositions in which a given predicate did simultaneously combine with one and two names to form propositions. We thus introduce the notion of an **n-placed** predicate stand-in (where, if a stand-in replaces "is red," for example, it is 1-placed, if it replaces "is taller than," it is 2-placed, and so on) and stipulate that any n-placed predicate stand-in immediately followed by n occurrences of name variables is a wff. Wherever a predicate stand-in occurs in what follows, we shall assume that it is of the proper number of places to combine successfully with as many occurrences of name variables as immediately follow it.

10.4 With wff's such as those so far specified, we have available a representation of the forms of propositions such as "Socrates is a man." These wff's enable us to represent what might be called **open propositional forms**, forms which require specification of both predicates and names to yield a proposition. More is required, however, to deal with "Every man is mortal," which is equally important to the logical truth of our example in 10.1. To regard this proposition as having a form representable as "fx" would involve treating "every man," which, allegories aside, is not the name of any man, let alone of every man, as a name. What we must be able to do is not only to **specify** the name variable in such a form, but to **quantify** over it as well. To take, for the moment, a simpler example than "Every man is mortal" — where a form of "Socrates is a man" is representable as "fx," a form of "Everything is a man" is "Everything is f," "For everything, it is f," or, using the machinery already available, "For every x, fx." [5]

---

[5] It has occurred to some philosophers to try to deal with the form of this proposition by regarding it as saying of each thing individually that it is a man. Its form, then, would be representable as an indefinitely long conjunctive formula (depending on how many "things" there are), thus: "KKKfxfyfzfu . . . ." See Wittgenstein [50], 5.3ff. For the difficulties raised by this attempt, see Pitcher [32], pp. 56–68.

In order to introduce this new notion "for every x" into our system, we require a new logical constant called the **universal quantifier**, consisting of an upper-case "A" followed by a single name variable (for example, "Ax," "Az," and so on) and to be read "for every x," "for every z," and so on. (There should be no confusion of this use of "A" with our earlier one. When an "A" occurs immediately followed by a name variable, it represents this quantificational notion; otherwise, it represents the propositional connective already discussed.) The formation rule for this constant is like that for "N"; it applies to the wff immediately following, or, as is often said, its **scope** is the wff immediately following. Thus the wff "Axfx" represents a form of "Everything is a man." (This form could equally well be represented as "Ayfy," of course.) We may say that wff's such as these represent **quantified propositional forms**, forms which may be turned into propositions merely by specifying what is to replace predicate stand-ins, since we have already quantified over name variables instead of specifying them.

We shall also introduce a symbol of similar construction, except with an upper-case "E" rather than an upper-case "A," to be read "there is an x (y, z, etc.) such that" or "for some x (y, z, etc.)" This logical constant will be called the **existential quantifier**.[6] When we come to add these quantifiers to our system by giving introduction and elimination rules for them, we shall define the existential quantifier in terms of the universal quantifier and show how to derive the rules for the existential quantifier. For present purposes, however, it is useful to have both symbols available.

When we come to state our rules for these notions, a very important distinction will be that between a **bound** and a **free** occurrence of a name variable. We shall say that an occurrence of a name variable is bound if it occurs as part of a quantifier, and it is bound by a quantifier if it occurs, not already otherwise bound, within the scope of a quantifier which includes an occurrence of that same name variable. An occurrence of a variable is free if it is not bound. Thus, in "Axfx,"

6 The decision to investigate the properties of "there is at least one" or "for at least one thing" rather than, say, "for some," where this implies "for *more* than one," is motivated by considerations like those which led us to concentrate on the inclusive rather than the exclusive "or." (See above, 5.5 and 5.8.) The reader is left to work out this suggestion for himself. There are relations between our quantifier and the inclusive "or" like those between the universal quantifier and "and" mentioned in the preceding note.

"AyExfxy," and "Axp," all occurrences of name variables are bound; in the second example, the second occurrence of "x" is bound by the existential quantifier and the second occurrence of "y" is bound by the universal quantifier. In "Afxgx" and "Cfxgy" all occurrences of name variables are free. In "KAxfxgx" the first two occurrences of "x" are bound while the last one is free. (Why?)

A few observations need to be made concerning these rules and distinctions. First of all, it is clear that, so long as there is any free occurrence of a name variable in a wff, it represents an open propositional form rather than a quantified propositional form. Only when all occurrences of name variables are bound does the result represent a quantified propositional form. Some care must be taken when quantifiers occur within the scope of other quantifiers, a clear possibility according to our formation rules and essential if these notions are to do all the work they can. For example, in "ExKfxAxgx" the second occurrence of "x" is bound by the existential quantifier while the fourth occurrence of "x" is bound by the universal quantifier. These relations might be made more perspicuous by writing instead the equivalent formula "ExKfxAygy." Similar remarks apply to an earlier example, "KAxfxgx," for which "KAxfxgy" might serve better. There is, however, no theoretical ambiguity in the original expressions.

Our rules also allow such expressions as "Axp" and "Axgy," in which there are no occurrences of the appropriate name variable for the quantifier to bind. It may seem difficult to make sense of such expressions; at the very least, the quantifiers seem to be doing no real work. In fact, such expressions can in general be shown to be equivalent to expressions which do not have such "free-floating" quantifiers, but it is convenient to allow such strings of symbols to be wff's.

Finally, we remark that no provision has been made here for treating predicate stand-ins as variables and quantifying over them. The definition of many more notions, particularly many of those useful in mathematics, requires this extension of the system or something comparable to it, but this procedure, which raises all kinds of interesting philosophical and technical questions, is beyond the scope of this work.[7]

The system which is to be obtained by adding (i) name variables, predicate stand-ins, and quantifiers with formation rules for them to

---

[7] For the philosophical questions, connected with problems about universals such as those mentioned in 10.2, see Quine [37], Ch. I and Ch. VI. For the technical development, see Hilbert and Ackermann [20], Ch. IV.

the symbols and formation rules for the propositional calculus, (ii) underived rules for universal quantifier introduction and elimination to
the underived rules for the propositional calculus, (iii) a definition of
the existential quantifier to the definitions in the propositional calculus,
and (iv) derived rules for existential quantifier introduction and elimination to the derived rules of the propositional calculus, will be called
the **predicate calculus.**

10.5   Before we proceed to develop the predicate calculus, it
will be a good idea to indicate briefly the power of the devices we
have introduced to represent various kinds of complicated propositions
in ordinary discourse. The issues involved here, like those in 5.8, will
be of two different kinds. One concerns the connections between the
constants formally defined in the system and the concepts they are
supposed to represent. This kind of issue is comparable to that concerning the connections between, say, "if . . . then" and "C." Like that
issue, it can only be discussed after we understand the properties of
our formally defined constants by seeing what wff's involving them are
theorems. The other kind of issue concerns the paraphrase of many
items in ordinary discourse as involving only the concepts, such as
"every" and the various propositional connectives, of which we intend
to offer formal accounts. This issue is comparable to that concerning,
say, the representation of the logical structure of many propositions
involving "but" and "nevertheless" in terms of "and." It is rather
more complicated in this case than in 5.8; rather more reflection is
required to see how we can deal with many propositions using the
notions "for everything" and "for something." For this reason we shall
discuss this issue briefly before we turn to the formal system.

It will be recalled that we began by developing an apparatus to
deal with name-predicate propositions, those with open forms, and extended it at least to deal with relatively uncomplicated propositions with
quantified forms, such as "Everything is a man." We chose this simple ·
example advisedly when introducing the notion of quantification, but
it may seem that there are very few interesting propositions about
everything. We have yet to deal with "Every man is mortal," for
example, which is one of the essential steps in dealing with the logical
truth of our example in 10.1. We must now see how useful our apparatus will be.

First, note that, in our symbolization, the "attributive tie" between name and predicate (which can be represented in many different
grammatical guises depending on whether the grammatical predicate

of the sentence is a noun, an adjective, or a verb, for example) simply vanishes into the adjunction of our two symbols. Similarly our "logical" predicates can be represented in many different ways grammatically, and very complicated ones can often be replaced by single predicate stand-ins. Thus "John runs," "John is taller than Mary," "John is tall," "John is a man," and "John is the first person in the class to get the right answer" may all be seen as having a form represented by the wff "fx." For some purposes, of course, the second example will be more perspicuously regarded as having a form representable as "fxy," and the last example will often require a still more searching analysis. Here, as in other cases, there is no simple rule for determining when a given analysis of logical form is to be preferred to an equally possible one.[8]

Next it should be observed that many occurrences of "each," "any," "every," and "all" may be represented in terms of the notion "for everything." Thus "Each thing is red," "Everything is red," "For anything at all, it is red," "All things are red" may all be paraphrased as "For everything, it is red," whose form will be represented by the quantificational formula "Axfx." (We list the quantificational formula as well as the paraphrase whose form it is supposed to represent, though the question of the accuracy of that representation must remain open until we have developed the system formally.) There will often be cases, however, where ambiguities must be resolved or care taken, some of which will be considered shortly. In a similar way many propositions beginning with "something," "at least one," and so on, can be rendered in terms of the notion "for something," which our existential quantifier is to represent.

The first important way of expanding what we can do with our fundamental notion is to complicate the wff's which come within the scope of our quantifiers by taking advantage of the fact that our formation rules permit those wff's to contain propositional connectives. Thus, for example, where "Some man is mortal" cannot be paraphrased as "Something is a man" or "Something is mortal," it can be paraphrased as "Something is both a man and mortal." The form of such a proposition can then be represented as the quantificational formula "ExKfxgx." (Of course any difficulties concerning connections between propositional connectives and their formal representatives will be relevant

---

[8] See Quine [38], pp. 157–161, reprinted as Selection 21 in Iseminger [21].

here and in similar cases.) Similar treatment can be accorded to "Some man is not mortal," "Something both is a man and it's not the case that it's mortal," "ExKfxNgx." These are examples of two of the kinds of **categorical propositions**, with which logic has largely been concerned through most of its history. The others, examples of which are "Every man is mortal" and "No man is mortal," may be paraphrased as open conditionals of the sort mentioned in 5.8, respectively, "For everything, if it is a man, then it is mortal" and "For everything, if it is a man, then it's not the case that it is mortal," "AxCfxgx" and "AxCfxNgx." This way of dealing with these propositions is by no means universally accepted; in Appendix A there is a discussion of some of the consequences of dealing with them in this way and a comparison of this account with more traditional accounts.

Now we can deal with one of the difficulties mentioned above when we were discussing "every," "all," and their relatives. Consider the difference between "If anything falls, it breaks" and "If anything falls, I'll jump." The first, assuming the "it" to be governed by "anything," is an open conditional, paraphrasable as "For everything, if it falls, then it breaks" ("AxCfxgx"), whereas the second is paraphrasable as "If there is something such that it falls, then I'll jump" ("CExfxp"). Moreover, the proposition "If something falls, it breaks" is probably, whatever appearances to the contrary, paraphrasable as the universally quantified proposition just discussed whose form was represented as "AxCfxgx." Again there are no handy rules for recognizing different logical forms behind similar grammatical forms or vice versa; the ultimate test will be whether a claim that two propositions expressed by sentence-types of similar grammatical forms are really of differing logical forms can be cashed in terms of different sort of entailments being seen to hold with regard to them.

Many propositions which appear to be of the name-predicate sort that our apparatus was initially developed to deal with turn out not to yield so readily to that analysis. Propositions containing **definite descriptions**, like "the Queen of England in 1966," rather than names, like "Queen Elizabeth II," raise difficulties which can best be appreciated if we take as an example "The King of France in 1966 is bald," where there is nothing of the sort described. In cases like this we may be tempted to say that the proposition is false precisely because there is not such a thing. One way our analysis could be made to accord with this feeling is to make the proposition in part a straightforward assertion that there is such a thing, thus: "There is something which is the King of France in 1966" ("Exfx"). The falsity of this part of the proposition would then account for the falsity of the whole. It has also been suggested that the proposition asserts that there is only one such being. Such an assertion can be paraphrased as "For everything, if it's the King of France in 1966, then it's identical to the first thing mentioned." Representing the form of this proposition requires a new symbol, one for the notion of **identity**, with which we shall not deal in this book but which we can take as "I" and regard quite plausibly as joining two name variables.[9] This form can then be represented as "AyCfyIxy." We must now add the assertion that the first entity mentioned is bald, "gx," and, putting the assertions together in such a way that the existential quantifier binds all the occurrences of the name variable it contains, we get "There is something such that it is the King of France in 1966 and such that both everything which is the King of France in 1966 is identical to it and it is bald." The form of this proposition can then be represented as "ExKfxKAyCfyIxygx."

We may now observe that many apparent names seem rather to be such descriptions in disguise, since we are often unsure whether there is any entity thus named. "Homer" is an example. If we accept the principle that a proposition about Homer has the same relation to his existence as a proposition about the King of France in 1966 has to his existence, we will replace "Homer" with, say, "the author of the *Iliad* and the *Odyssey*" and analyze it as we did our earlier example about the King of France in 1966. From here it is but a short step to argue that, even where names apply to existing things, the "existential commitments," as we may say, of applying names can best be made explicit by replacing all putative names with descriptive phrases and analyzing them in this fashion. The faintly paradoxical result is that an apparatus originally developed to deal with name-predicate propositions may finally be applied in such a way as to suggest that in the last analysis there really are no propositions of that form.[10]

Finally it is worth noting that the attributive "is," which has been represented by the adjunction of predicate stand-ins and name variables in our formulas, and "there is," which our existential quantifier

[9] For formal treatment of the concept of identity, see Suppes [46], pp. 101–108.

[10] For controversies surrounding this rendering, essentially due to Russell, of so-called *definite descriptions*, see Russell in Feigl and Sellars [13], Strawson, Selection 14 in Ammerman [1], and Quine [38], pp. 176–186.

is intended to represent, are both timeless and therefore tenseless notions. Nor do we have separate quantifiers for "there was something," "there will be something," and so on. These facts are not surprising when one realizes that many of the people who developed the apparatus of modern logic were mainly concerned with dealing with mathematical statements, having forms such as "There is a number such that . . ." and "The sum is . . .," where time and tense are clearly irrelevant. Nonetheless, where the temporal force of a proposition is an important part of its "logical powers," there are ways of dealing with it while still retaining our atemporal attributive ties and quantifiers.[11]

To deal with this issue and other similar ones, however, would require a more complex discussion than is now appropriate. The reader who wishes to delve more deeply into these and other proposed paraphrases in terms of our limited set of notions should remember that the important issue is only whether or not in making the paraphrase, however grammatically awkward it may seem, we come out with something which does in fact represent the "logical powers" of the proposition we began with. Really to answer a question of this kind, of course, we must know more about the behavior of our formally introduced notions; we turn, therefore, to the development of their properties in the predicate calculus.

[11] For a discussion of ways of dealing with the temporal force of propositions in terms of the atemporal apparatus of the predicate calculus, see Quine [38], pp. 170–176.

11

Predicate calculus

11.1 We turn now to the formal development of the properties of our new constants. Here, as with our earlier systems, we want as theorems all and only wff's which represent the forms of logically true propositions whose logical truth depends on the concepts our symbols are to represent. With theorems involving only proposition stand-ins and truth-functional or modal constants, the forms to be represented were forms such that no matter what propositions replaced the stand-ins the resulting proposition was true. Similarly with theorems involving our new constants, stand-ins, and variables, the forms to be represented will be forms such that no matter what predicates replace the predicate stand-ins and no matter what names replace the free occurrences of name variables (the same predicate for a given stand-in and the same name for a given variable throughout, of course), the result is a true proposition.[1] (Since proposition stand-ins can occur in theorems in the predicate calculus, too, we must also add a clause to the effect that any theorem containing proposition stand-ins must still represent a form such that no matter what propositions replace the

---

[1] There are difficulties with this attempt to characterize the wff's we want to be theorems in the predicate calculus, most of which involve forms such that propositions of those forms would not be true in what has been called "the empty universe." See Suppes [46], pp. 67–68, and the articles in Iseminger [21] referred to in note 9 below.

stand-ins, the same proposition for each occurrence of a given stand-in throughout, the resulting proposition is true.)

In the case of our earlier wff's involving only truth-functional connectives and proposition stand-ins, we developed a decision procedure, the truth table test, which, it was argued, enabled us to decide whether a given form involving those concepts carried logical truth with it by seeing whether the wff representing that form was a ttt. In the present case there is, in general, no such decision procedure for wff's involving our new symbols,[2] but we can motivate our choice of introduction and elimination rules by giving a few examples of wff's we want to be theorems, given the above account, which says, in effect, that we want our theorems still to represent forms of propositions true in virtue of their form, where we have extended our analysis of "form" with our new apparatus. For example, the form of "If every man is mortal and Socrates is a man, then Socrates is mortal" will be represented by the wff "CKAxCfxgxfxgx," which we shall therefore want to be a theorem. The reader should test it intuitively by replacing predicate stand-ins and free occurrences of name variables with randomly chosen predicates and names, respectively, according to the instructions in the preceding paragraph, and seeing if the result of each such set of replacements is true. Another example, involving the notion of existential quantification, is "If John is both 6 feet tall and red-headed, then there is something which is red-headed." The form of this proposition may be represented by the wff "CKfxgxExgx," which we shall want to be a theorem and which should be intuitively tested in the same way. The reader may wish to find other examples, but these should suffice to give us some idea of what sort of wff's we want to be theorems in the predicate calculus.

11.2 We turn now to the rules for the universal quantifier, beginning with AxE, which is intuitively fairly obvious: if a predicate applies to anything whatsoever, then it applies to any particular thing we might choose. In formal terms, we may simply drop the universal quantifier, moving, for example, from "AxCfxgx" to "Cfxgx." It will also be permissible to move from "AxCfxgx" to, say, "Cfygy." We can schematize this rule as follows:

---

[2] There are, however, decision procedures for certain special cases involving quantification. See Kneale and Kneale [22], pp. 724ff.

(AxE) ·|·   ·

m Axp Ri

n p (or any wff just like p ex-   AxE, m
cept that all free occur-
rences of "x" in p are
replaced by occurrences
of some other one name
variable.)

With this rule and the rules and definition which follow, we must take it as stated for the case as above except with "y," or "z," etc., for each occurrence of "x" in the above schema (except that it does not matter whether in justifying the step we call the rule "AxE," or "AyE," or "AzE," etc.) We shall not state this generalization explicitly in what follows.

Here are some examples of proper applications of this rule.

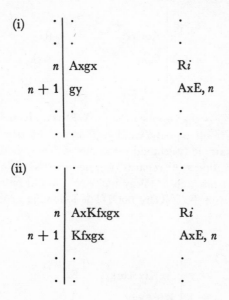

(i) ·|·   ·

n Axgx   Ri

$n+1$ gy   AxE, n

(ii) ·|·   ·

n AxKfxgx   Ri

$n+1$ Kfxgx   AxE, n

(iii)

	.	.
	.	.
n	Axfxy	Ri
$n + 1$	fxy	AxE, n
$n + 2$	fyy	AxE, n
	.	.
	.	.

(iv)

	.	.
	.	.
n	AxKfxAxgx	Ri
$n + 1$	KfyAxgx	AxE, n
	.	.
	.	.

(v)

	.	.
	.	.
n	AyCpq	Ri
$n + 1$	Cpq	AxE, n
	.	.
	.	.

Example (iii) shows that application of AxE to a given step can yield more than one result equally validly. This will be true of our other rules as well. Example (v) should recall our earlier remarks concerning free-floating quantifiers. As regards (iv), neither "Kfygy" nor "Kfxgx" follows directly from step n. (Why not?) Nor would either one follow directly from step $n + 1$. (Why not?) The following procedure would yield "Kfygy."

	.	.
	.	.
n	AxKfxAxgx	Ri
$n + 1$	KfyAxgx	AxE, n
$n + 2$	fy	KE, $n + 1$

$n + 3$	Axgx	KE, $n + 1$
$n + 4$	gy	AxE, $n + 3$
$n + 5$	Kfygy	KI, $n + 2, n + 4$
.	.	.
.	.	.

The rule of AxI is not so easy to state. Clearly, we do not want a simple converse of AxE, for this would involve the (obviously false) claim that some predicate's being applicable to one particular thing entailed the predicate's being applicable to anything whatsoever. What we require is a new kind of subordinate proof called a **general proof**, said to be general **with respect to** some name variable, having no hypothesis and involving the restriction that nothing containing a free occurrence of a name variable may be borrowed into a proof general with respect to that name variable. Such a proof is indicated by writing the name variable with respect to which the proof is general to the left of the proof's vertical line. The rule of AxI states that anything inside such a proof may be written outside it, in the proof to which the general proof is immediately subordinate, prefixed by the universal quantifier containing the name variable with respect to which the proof is general. Schematically:

$$(AxI)$$

(AxI) ·	.	.
	.	.
l	x	.	.
	.	.
	.	.
m	p	Ri
	.	.
	.	.
	.	.
	.	.
n	Axp	AxI, l—m
	.	.
	.	.

The intuitive justification of the rule is this: the restriction on borrowing insures that we will not be able to use information merely about a predicate's applying to some particular thing in proving that it applies to everything. Another way of saying much the same thing is to say that, without such a restriction, the rule of AxI would immediately become a simple converse of AxE (why?), and we agreed that this would be undesirable. In order to write down, say, "AxAfxNfx," we must derive "AfxNfx" from "general" considerations, much as we had to derive "ApNp" from "necessary" conditions (inside a strict proof) in order to write down "LApNp."[3]

Following are some valid applications of this rule (provided always that no illicit borrowings have been made).

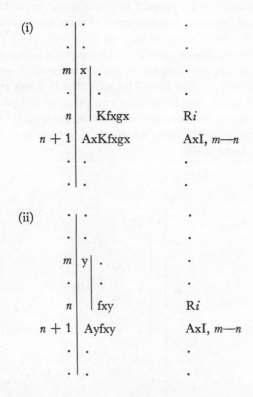

	(i)	·	·	·
		·	·	·
m	x	·	·	
		·	·	·
n			Kfxgx	Ri
$n+1$			AxKfxgx	AxI, m—n
		·	·	·
		·	·	·

	(ii)	·		·
		·	·	·
m	y	·	·	·
		·	·	·
n			fxy	Ri
$n+1$			Ayfxy	AxI, m—n
		·	·	·
		·	·	·

---

[3] The parallelism between this rule and LI, and between the definition of "M" in terms of "L" and the definition below of "Ex" in terms of "Ax," and similar parallelisms, suggest connections between modalities and quantifiers which are worth reflecting on. See Prior [34], pp. 188ff.

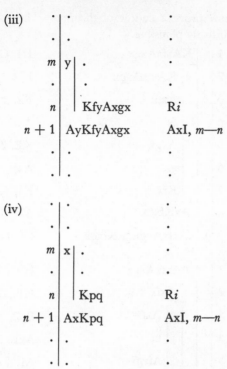

(iii)

	·	·	·
	·	·	·
m	y	·	·
	·	·	·
n		KfyAxgx	Ri
$n+1$	AyKfyAxgx		AxI, m—n
	·	·	·
	·	·	·

(iv)

	·	·	·
	·	·	·
m	x	·	·
	·	·	·
n		Kpq	Ri
$n+1$	AxKpq		AxI, m—n
	·	·	·
	·	·	·

Note the last example and recall again our remarks about free-floating quantifiers. The removability of any such non-working universal quantifier should now be apparent; that is, we can prove EAxpp where p contains no free occurrences of "x." The following example is not valid. (Why not?) Nonetheless, step $n + 1$ can eventually be obtained from the material given. (How?)

(v)

	·	·	·
	·	·	·
m	x	·	·
	·	·	·
n		Kfxgx	Ri
$n+1$	KfxAxgx		AxI, m—n (invalid)
	·	·	·
	·	·	·

We can now prove a couple of theorems. The reader is left to make them intuitively plausible.

(49)	1	KAxfxAxgx	HP(CI)
	2	x KAxfxAxgx	B, 1
	3	Axfx	KE, 2
	4	fx	AxE, 3
	5	Axgx	KE, 2
	6	gx	AxE, 5
	7	Kfxgx	KI, 4, 6
	8	AxKfxgx	AxI, 2—7
	9	CKAxfxAxgxAxKfxgx	CI, 1—8

(50)	1	AAxfxAxgx	HP(CI)
	2	Axfx	HP(AE)
	3	x Axfx	B, 2
	4	fx	AxE, 3
	5	Afxgx	AI, 4
	6	AxAfxgx	AxI, 3—5
	7	Axgx	HP(AE)
	8	x Axgx	B, 7
	9	gx	AxE, 8
	10	Afxgx	AI, 9
	11	AxAfxgx	AxI, 8—10
	12	AxAfxgx	AE, 1, 2—6, 7—11
	13	CAAxfxAxgxAxAfxgx	CI, 1—12

The converse of (49),

(51) CAxKfxgxKAxfxAxgx,

is a theorem whose proof is left to the reader. The converse of (50) is not a theorem. The reader should convince himself that the proof cannot be constructed and see intuitively why it would not be desirable as a theorem.

11.3   The existential quantifier will be defined as follows:

D7.   Exp and NAxNp are equivalent by definition.

This definition will make intuitive sense if we recall that the notion symbolized by "Ex" is "there is at least one."

The rule of existential quantifier introduction is as simple as the rule of universal quantifier·elimination. If a predicate applies to a particular thing, we can assert that it applies to something. The rule may be represented schematically as follows, where p is by definition what follows "Ex" in step n:

(ExI)	⋮ ⋮		⋮
m	p	(or any wff just like p except that all free occurrences of "x" in p are replaced by occurrences of some other one name variable.)	Ri
⋮ ⋮	⋮ ⋮		⋮
n	Exp		ExI, m
⋮ ⋮	⋮ ⋮		⋮

The reader is left to derive ExI if he wishes, using the rules of the propositional calculus together with D7 and AxE.

Some valid applications of ExI are as follows:

(i)

	⋮ ⋮	⋮
n	Nfx	Ri
$n+1$	ExNfx	ExI, n
	⋮ ⋮	⋮

(ii)

	⋮ ⋮	⋮
n	KfyExgx	Ri
$n+1$	EyKfyExgx	ExI, n
$n+2$	ExKfxExgx	ExI, n
	⋮ ⋮	⋮

(iii)

	·	·
	·	·
n	Kfxgx	Ri
$n+1$	EyKfygx	ExI, n
$n+2$	EyKfygy	ExI, n
	·	·
	·	·

The following are invalid applications of ExI, although in (iv) step $n+1$ could be got from n eventually:

(iv)

	·	·
	·	·
n	Kfxgx	Ri
$n+1$	KfxExgx	ExI, n (invalid)
	·	·
	·	·

(v)

	·	·
	·	·
n	Kfxgy	Ri
$n+1$	EyKfygy	ExI, n (invalid)
	·	·
	·	·

The following theorem is now immediately provable:

(52)	1	Axfx	HP(CI)
	2	fx	AxE, 1
	3	Exfx	ExI, 2
	4	CAxfxExfx	CI, 1—3

The rule of ExE will obviously not be a simple converse of ExI; we do not want to be able to infer from the fact that a predicate applies to something or other that it applies to any particular thing. The rule of ExE states that from Exp together with a subordinate proof (i) general with respect to "x," (ii) having as a hypothesis p, and (iii) having a step q which does not contain any free occurrences of "x," we may infer q. Schematically:

(ExE)

	·	·	·
	·	·	·
k	Exp		Ri
	·	·	·
	·	·	·
l	x	p	HP(ExE)
		·	·
	·	·	·
	·	·	·
m		q (containing no free occurrences of "x.")	Rj
	·	·	·
	·	·	·
n	q		ExE, k, l—m
	·	·	·
	·	·	·

Consider the (usual) case where p contains a free occurrence of "x"; let us say it is "fx." Having the subordinate proof general with respect to "x" and with a hypothesis "fx" means, roughly, that no matter what individual we consider, if the predicate signified by "f" can be applied to it, we can conclude that q. (The derivation of ExE, which is left to the reader, would show that appearing to permit a general proof to have a hypothesis is, like the similar maneuver with strict proofs in ME and C'I, an avoidable shortcut. The hypothesis really belongs to a CI proof.) Since step k tells us that the predicate signified by "f" applies to something, that step together with the subordinate proof l—m justifies us in concluding that q. If q were permitted to contain a free occurrence of "x," however, the obviously undesirable (why?) result "CExfxfx" would immediately be provable as a theorem (how?), and the derivation of the rule could not be carried out.[4]

Here is a proof employing ExE. Theorem (53) represents the form of a proposition such as "If all men are mortal and there are men, then there are mortals."

(53)	1	KAxCfxgxExfx	HP(CI)
	2	AxCfxgx	KE, 1
	3	Exfx	KE, 1
	4	x | fx	HP(ExE)
	5	AxCfxgx	B, 2
	6	Cfxgx	AxE, 5
	7	gx	CE, 4, 6
	8	Exgx	ExI, 7
	9	Exgx	ExE, 3, 4—8
	10	CKAxCfxgxExfxExgx	CI, 1—9

Some remarks about the strategy of this proof are in order. Our problem reduced to getting from a universally quantified wff (step 2) and an existentially quantified wff (step 3) to another existentially quantified wff (step 9). There might appear to have been alternative procedures available; the reader should convince himself that alternatives, such as applying AxE to step 2 before borrowing it or using ExI as the overall strategy to get step 9, would not work. A general strategic maxim is: do not use AxE until necessary, and when the problem is to get from (among other things) one existentially quantified wff to another, use ExE as the strategy, reserving ExI for use as a tactical maneuver.

---

[4] Another way of making ExE plausible depends on a relation between "Ex" and "A" like that mentioned between "Ax" and "K" in note 5 to Chapter 10 above. ExE can be regarded as a kind of infinite AE proof. The reader may work this suggestion out for himself.

11.4 We now have all the apparatus necessary for operating in our predicate calculus, and we can proceed to prove theorems. In all the following, the reader is again urged to prove those theorems which are proved in the text and convince himself that they ought to be theorems, that is, that they represent forms which carry logical truth and in which "every" and "some" occur essentially. Similar consideration should be given to wff's which are said not to be theorems. (Again, these are not shown not to be theorems here.)

First, there is a group of theorems relating the quantifiers to one another through negation.[5]

(54) ENAxfxExNfx
(55) EAxfxNExNfx
(56) EAxNfxNExfx

The proof of (55) follows:

(55)			
1	Axfx		HP(EI)
2	ExNfx		HP(NI)
3	x	Nfx	HP(ExE)
4		Axfx	B, 1
5		fx	AxE, 4
6		NExNfx	NE (derived rule), 3, 5
7	NExNfx		ExE, 2, 3—6
8	NExNfx		NI, 2—7 (2, 7)
9	NExNfx		HP(EI)
10	x	Nfx	HP(NI)
11		ExNfx	ExI, 10
12		NExNfx	B, 9
13	NNfx		NI, 10—12 (11, 12)
14	fx		NNE, 13
15	Axfx		AxI, 10—14
16	EAxfxNExNfx		EI, 1—8, 9—15

[5] If the reader reflects on the relations between "Ax" and "K" and between "Ex" and "A," as hinted at in the preceding note and in note 5 to Chapter 10, he will see that these theorems parallel earlier theorems. Compare, for example, (24) and (56).

With the existence of predicates of more than one place, there arise possibilities of more than one quantifier appearing at the beginning of a wff and interesting questions as to the significance of the order in which quantifiers occur.

(57)	1	ExEyfxy	HP(EI)
	2	x Eyfxy	HP(ExE)
	3	y fxy	HP(ExE)
	4	Exfxy	ExI, 3
	5	EyExfxy	ExI, 4
	6	EyExfxy	ExE, 2, 3—5
	7	EyExfxy	ExE, 1, 2—6
	8	EyExfxy	HP(EI)
	9	y Exfxy	HP(ExE)
	10	x fxy	HP(ExE)
	11	Eyfxy	ExI, 10
	12	ExEyfxy	ExI, 11
	13	ExEyfxy	ExE, 9, 10—12
	14	ExEyfxy	ExE, 8, 9—13
	15	EExEyfxyEyExfxy	EI, 1—7, 8—14

We can also easily prove

(58) EAxAyfxyAyAxfxy.

When the quantifiers are different, the questions are a little more complicated.

(59) CExAyfxyAyExfxy

can be proved, but the converse, and hence the equivalence, cannot.

Some other theorems follow:

(60) EExAfxgxAExfxExgx
(61) CExKfxgxKExfxExgx
(62) CAxCfxpCAxfxp
(63) EExKfxpKExfxp

(64) ECpAxfxAxCpfx
(65) ExAfxNfx

The converses of (61) and (62) are not theorems.

11.5 If we represent the forms of categorical propositions as suggested in 10.5, it becomes possible to show the validity of various entailment claims involving such propositions. Claims involving these propositions and some of the controversies surrounding them are discussed in Appendix A. Here we only indicate how the validity of some of them may be shown in our calculus, given the proposed way of representing the forms of these propositions in terms of the apparatus now available. The reader should prove these theorems and, after reading Appendix A, discover and prove theorems representing other traditionally sanctioned forms of inference.

One part of the traditional doctrine of categorical propositions involved so-called **immediate inferences**. One of the claims here was that, for example, "No men are mortal" and "No mortals are men" are equivalent. To show its validity under the present conditions would be to prove the following theorem:

(66) EAxCfxNgxAxCgxNfx

Another part of the doctrine involved the so-called **square of opposition**. One of the claims here was that "Every man is mortal" is equivalent to "It's not the case that some man is not mortal." The theorem to be proved in the predicate calculus is

(67) EAxCfxgxNExKfxNgx.

The most familiar part of the doctrine involved the **syllogism**. We may take as an example of a syllogism whose validity was claimed, "If every man is mortal and some man is an American, then some American is mortal." The theorem to be proved is

(68) CKAxCfxgxExKfxhxExKhxgx.

Finally, we show the validity of the example which appears in 10.1 (which was what moved us to take up quantifiers in the first place) "If every man is mortal and Socrates is a man, then Socrates is mortal."[6]

---

[6] This example was taken to be a syllogism in many versions of the traditional doctrine, but Aristotle did not regard it as such. (See Łukasiewicz [24], pp. 1–7.) For further discussion of the syllogism, see Appendix A below. For reasons for regarding the example as a syllogism, see Strawson [45], pp. 179–181. For arguments against so regarding it, see Russell [43], pp. 197–198.

(69)	1	KAxCfxgxfx	HP(CI)
	2	AxCfxgx	KE, 1
	3	Cfxgx	AxE, 2
	4	fx	KE, 1
	5	gx	CE, 3, 4
	6	CKAxCfxgxfxgx	CI, 1—5

11.6 Now that we have a sample of the theorems of our system and of the consequent claims about logical truths involving such concepts as "all," "every," "some," "there exists," and so on, we can consider briefly the question of the adequacy of our formally defined quantifiers to the concepts they are supposed to represent. Most of these questions surround the existential quantifier in its guise as a formal representation of "some" or "there exists."

One question concerns the implication of plurality which appears to attach to the notion "some" but does not attach to the notion represented by "Ex." This question is rather like that about the alleged implication of exclusiveness which attaches to "or," and it can be dealt with, in part at least, in much the same way. (This should not be surprising in view of the relations between the existential quantifier and disjunction discussed in some of our footnotes.) Thus one justification for choosing the notion we do choose to represent in our system is that it enters into relationships with the universal quantifier of the sort which make D7 plausible. Further, it may be argued, most entailment relations involving "some" propositions depend on that aspect of the concept which may be expressed as "at least one" and not on any further aspect of the concept expressible as "more than one." Finally, if, for particular purposes, it is thought important to capture the notion of plurality in representing a proposition, the present quantifier can be used in a paraphrase which recalls our discussion in 10.5 of the alleged implication of uniqueness in propositions involving definite descriptions. A paraphrase of "Some man is mortal" using only the present quantifier and representing the proposition in such a way that it entails that more than one man is mortal would be "There is something which is a man and is mortal, and there is something which is a man and is mortal and is not identical to the first thing mentioned" ("ExEyKKKfxgxKfygyNIyx"). Dealing with this paraphrase formally, of course, would require that we have the notion of identity in our system.

Somewhat more serious questions surround the existential quantifier in its role as a formal representation of "there exists." One issue which arises here is whether there is a single sense of "exists" being employed in such statements as "There exists a prime number greater than 3," "The King of France in 1966 does not exist," "Being a Man (as opposed to an individual man) exists," and "Mental events exist but are not located in space." Philosophers have argued on various grounds that different senses of "exist" are involved in these propositions, a suggestion which would seem to run contrary to the supposition made by most logicians that all of these propositions can be rendered using the existential quantifier to represent "exist" as it occurs in them.[7]

A consequence which is often drawn from the standard way of rendering explicit existential claims in terms of the apparatus of our system may be summed up in the claim that *"exists" is not a predicate.* Existential claims such as "The Queen of England exists," or "There is a Queen of England," are usually paraphrased in terms of our quantifier as "There is something such that it is the Queen of England," "Exfx." If we restrict the term "predicate" to concepts for which our predicate stand-ins are stand-ins, this way of dealing with such propositions clearly does make "exists" into something other than a predicate, for the only predicate stand-in in this formula is a stand-in for "is the Queen of England." This analysis of existential propositions has consequences for the so-called **ontological argument** for the existence of God, which, in one of its forms at least, seems to depend upon taking "exists" to be a predicate in the present sense of that term. Another consequence of this analysis is to make such apparently perfectly comprehensible propositions as "Something exists" opaque to analysis to the point where one is tempted to say that they do not make sense at all, or at least not in the way they appear to. Whether these consequences are merits or defects of the analysis, I shall not here discuss.[8]

The difficulty with "something exists," of course, is that it appears to treat as two concepts what quantificational logic, on its usual inter-

[7] For views which, often on radically different grounds, distinguish senses of "exists," see the selections by Russell and Meinong in Iseminger [21] and Ryle [44], p. 23. For a defense of the logician's rendering of "there exists," see the selection by White in Iseminger [21].

[8] See Kneale in Feigl and Sellars [13] and Malcolm's discussion of the ontological argument in [25] for discussion of these issues.

pretation, tells us we should treat as one, the concepts "some" and "there is." In particular, of course, it seems that this proposition says that the predicate "exists" applies to something. (We must not be too readily seduced by grammatical forms, of course.) If the first question about our quantifier and its relation to "exists" concerned its adequacy to what some have taken to be the many different senses of "exists," we must now ask whether it is adequate to *any* sense of "exists," whether the usual interpretation of "Ex" does not involve confusing the quantificational notion "some" or "at least one," which our symbol does seem to represent, with the predicate "exists," which it may seem less suited to represent.

There are reasons for asking this question other than a desire to be able to give an analysis of "Something exists" which preserves its sense and accords fairly closely with its superficial grammatical form. These reasons involve doubts about theorems, like (65), which begin with our so-called existential quantifier. The problem may be stated summarily as follows: (i) theorems of our system are supposed to represent logical truths; (ii) logical truths are true irrespective of the facts or of what exists; (iii) propositions of the form represented by (65), however, would not be true if nothing existed, since they manifestly assert that something does. From these premises we may conclude that propositions of the form represented by (65) are not logical truths according to (ii) and that (65), therefore, should not be a theorem according to (i). There are several possible moves in the face of this dilemma. One could argue with the criterion of logical truth advanced in (ii) or argue that, when that criterion is properly understood, the existential claims made by propositions having the form represented by (65) do not violate it. Finally, one could argue that such propositions are not existential and thus escape the dilemma by denying (iii). To argue thus, of course, would be to separate our quantifier sharply from the notion of existence and to imply that the "existential" part of the term "existential quantifier" made this a misleading description of it.[9]

11.7 There are several directions in which one may go from this introduction to deductive logic.

[9] Quine [37], pp. 160ff, rejects the criterion; Cohen in Iseminger [21] argues that the existential claim does not violate it. Lejewski in Iseminger [21] denies that any existential claim is involved and develops a system which has the effect of treating "exists" as a predicate.

One of the main aims of modern logic at its inception was to show that mathematics could be "reduced to logic"; that is, that mathematical notions could be defined in terms of logical constants in the sense in which we have defined some logical constants in terms of other and that familiar truths of mathematics could then be shown to be logical truths. Thus, it was hoped, some mystery surrounding such propositions could be dispelled. The attempt to carry out this program requires additional apparatus, and thus further extending the system would be one way to proceed from here. The introduction of the notions of set (or class) and member (notions sometimes introduced before quantifiers and in terms of which quantifiers may be introduced) and the extension of the predicate calculus to permit quantification over predicate stand-ins are among the chief extensions usually made with this end in view, and these notions and operations with them raise many technical and philosophical questions of great interest.[10]

Another set of questions which arise, of course, concerns the metatheory of the modal propositional calculus and the predicate calculus, as well as of any further extensions.[11]

Again, logic, like any intellectual enterprise, did not emerge full-blown at its inception; it has a history. This history is a fascinating study, for the light it sheds on other philosophical doctrines of the philosopher-logicians of the past, for the ingenuity evident in much of past logic which has more or less been forgotten, and for the intimations of modern doctrine.[12]

Finally, the reflective reader may wish to go more deeply into the philosophical questions we have touched on throughout this book.[13] In whatever direction he chooses to pursue the further study of logic, or if he chooses not to do so, I hope he will have gotten from this book a sense of what remains to be studied and what remains to be done. It is truly meant to be an introduction.

[10] For a classic statement of this aim, see the "Introduction" (by Russell) to Whitehead and Russell [49]. For a more recent statement, see Quine [37], Chapter V. Suppes [46] is a textbook in which this aim is prominent. For philosophical questions which arise in pursuit of it, see many of the selections in Benacerraf and Putnam [6].

[11] For further discussion of modal and related systems, see Prior [34], pp. 185ff. The metatheory of the predicate calculus and higher-order predicate logic is dealt with in Hilbert and Ackermann [20], Chapters III and IV.

[12] Kneale and Kneale [22] is excellent in this area.

[13] Suggestions for readings in Iseminger [21] have been given for the most part as the questions arose.

Appendix A: CATEGORICAL PROPOSITIONS

Traditional logic, stemming from Aristotle, was developed with great ingenuity through the Middle Ages but became more or less stagnant after the seventeenth century. It consisted mainly of the theory of logical relations among what were known as **categorical propositions** (**cp's**), examples of which we have seen in 10.5. Such propositions consist of assertions about the relations between the things to which one predicate applies and things to which another predicate applies. (In our examples they were things to which "is a man" applies and things to which "is mortal" applies.) The logically relevant differences among cp's were felt, quite reasonably, to revolve around whether the proposition said something about all or some of the things to which the first predicate applied and whether the second predicate was said to apply or not to apply to them. The first difference was called a difference of **quantity**, the second, a difference of **quality**. When these differences are cross-classified, there result four different categorical propositions concerning, say, men and mortals in that order:

"Every man is mortal" is **affirmative** in quality and **universal** in quantity.
"No man is mortal" is **negative universal**.
"Some man is mortal" is **affirmative particular**.
"Some man is not mortal" is **negative particular**.

Note that the representation of forms of these propositions in the symbolism of the predicate calculus as suggested in 10.5 raises questions as to whether they can be distinguished as negative or affirmative in the manner just suggested. Certainly the sense in which the so-called negative propositions are distinguished from the affirmative propositions is not readily translatable in terms of the propositional connective "it's not the case that," which we have represented by the "N."

In representing forms of these propositions, no special symbols were used for the notions "every" and "some" or for "is" and "not," and only one kind of stand-in, the **term stand-in**, corresponding in intended interpretation roughly to our predicate stand-in, was used. Since we are proceeding quite informally now, we shall use appropriate upper-case letters more or less indiscriminately as these stand-ins. Each of the four forms of cp was identified according to the successive vowels in the Latin word indicating its quality, "Affirmo" ("I assert") and "Nego" ("I deny"), thus:

A: Every S is P.   E: No S is P.
I: Some S is P.   O: Some S is not P.

It must not be thought that, in dealing only with four forms of propositions, logicians were simply ignoring whole vast areas for logical investigation, for their ingenuity in showing that a proposition which did not appear to be a cp could in fact be regarded as having the logical powers of some cp was considerable.[1]

One set of questions logicians asked about cp's concerned what were called **immediate inferences**. One form of immediate inference, called **conversion**, consisted simply in interchanging the first term (the **subject**) and the second (the **predicate**). (Note that terms which are regarded indifferently as predicates in our analysis of cp's in terms of the apparatus of the predicate calculus are here distinguished into subjects and predicates.) The question had to be asked, of course, whether the proposition thus obtained, the **converse** of the original cp, did in fact follow from it. The standard doctrine was that the converse did follow validly from propositions of E and I forms (henceforth to be called simply E and I propositions), but not from A or O propositions. In fact, in the case of E or I propositions, it can be seen immediately that, if their converses follow from them, their converses are equivalent to them. (Why?) A related form of inference, called **conversion by limitation** (in Latin *conversio per accidens*) by contrast with **simple conversion** (*conversio simplex*), in which, in addition to the exchange of terms there was a change of quality from universal to particular, was held to be valid for the A, however. (The reader is again asked to check the laws of inference suggested against his intuitive ideas of the behavior of the notions involved.) In keeping with our present informality, we shall simply list valid patterns of argument,

[1] See, for example, Parker and Veatch [30], Chapter 11.

rather than giving "theorems." It will be as if in discussing propositional logic we had simply said, for example, that "p and q" entails "p" rather than turning this question into a question about logically true conditionals and giving formal accounts of the logical constants occurring essentially in such conditionals.

A: "Every S is P" entails "Some S is P" (valid conversion by limitation).

E: "No S is P" is equivalent to "No P is S" (valid simple conversion).

I: "Some S is P" is equivalent to "Some P is S" (valid simple conversion).

O: ... (no valid conversion).

In order to discuss the form of immediate inference called **obversion**, we must add to our apparatus a device for "negating a term," as we may say, rather than a proposition. This is most conveniently done by prefixing a "non-" to the original term, which yields another term, to be called the **complement** of the original term. The obverse of a cp is then obtained by changing its quality and substituting for the predicate its complement. For any cp, it was held, its obverse follows from it and is in fact equivalent to it, the latter claim following from the first if we accept a kind of NNE for terms.

A: "Every S is P" is equivalent to "No S is non-P" (valid obversion).

E: "No S is P" is equivalent to "Every S is non-P" (valid obversion).

I: "Some S is P" is equivalent to "Some S is not non-P" (valid obversion).

O: "Some S is not P" is equivalent to "Some S is non-P" (valid obversion).

With **contraposition** we are able to achieve the beginnings of systematization. The contrapositive of a cp is formed by first exchanging the two terms and then substituting for them their complements. The same result can be achieved by first obverting a cp, then converting the result, and finally obverting that result. Thus we can discover, as a derived principle, whether a cp's contrapositive follows from it by observing whether each of these operations can be performed validly in the order given according to the principles already stated. (Of course, only the conversion raises any questions.) The reader is left to derive these principles for himself.

The **square of opposition** concerns relations among A, E, I, and O propositions having the same subject and predicate. The A and O are said to be **contradictories** (that is, the one is equivalent to the denial of the other) as are the E and I.

"Every S is P" is equivalent to "It's not the case that some S is not P."

"Some S is P" is equivalent to "It's not the case that no S is P" (Here "it's not the case that" *is* the notion of negation as a propositional connective with which we are familiar.) The I is the **subaltern** of (follows from) the A, and similarly with the O and the E.

"Every S is P" entails "Some S is P."

"No S is P" entails "Some S is not P."

One of these principles of subalternation can be derived from the two principles of contradiction together with the other principle of subalternation. It is also possible from the same material to derive the principle which says that A and E are **contraries** (cannot both be true),

"Every S is P" entails "It's not the case that no S is P,"

and the principle which says that I and O are **subcontraries** (cannot both be false),

"It's not the case that some S is P" entails "Some S is not P."

The reader is left to work out these informal derivations.

Syllogistic inference was the main topic of traditional logic. It is fashionable now to belittle the importance of this form of inference.[2] There is no doubt that exaggerated claims have been made in its behalf, and it appeared only as an incidental part of what our system dealt with, but there is no gainsaying the number and variety of inferences which can be dealt with in the theory of the syllogism and the possibilities it provides for formal development.[3]

A syllogism consists of three cp's, one of which (the **conclusion**) is claimed to follow from the other two (the **premises**); these three cp's contain among them three terms: one (the **major** term, for which we shall ordinarily give the stand-in "P") occurs as the predicate of the conclusion and in one of the premises; another (the **minor** term, for which we shall ordinarily give the stand-in "S") occurs as the subject of the conclusion and in the other premise; the third (the **middle**

[2] See Russell [43], pp. 198–199. Parker and Veatch [30] is a recent textbook written from the standpoint of traditional logic and defending it against attacks by logicians such as Russell.

[3] See Łukasiewicz [24] and Bird [7].

term, for which we shall ordinarily give the stand-in "M") occurs once in each premise.

The aim of the doctrine of the syllogism is to discover what factors affect the validity of such inferences and then to discover and relate those of them which are valid. The first relevant factor, obviously, will be which cp's occur where. For example, "Some man is short" and "Some mortal being is a man," clearly do not entail "Every mortal being is short" simply because of this factor, and thus we can say that a syllogism is invalid simply on the grounds that its premises are I propositions and its conclusion an A. We symbolize this feature of the syllogism, called its **mood**, simply by listing in order the letters indicating the forms of the cp's of which it is made up, in this case, IIA. Since there are four such forms and three cp's in a syllogism, there are 4^3 or 64 possible moods.

If mood were the only factor relevant to the validity of a syllogism, we would now simply have to decide which of these moods are valid and then for any given syllogism see whether or not it is in one of the valid moods. In fact, however, there are other relevant factors. For example, "Every man is mortal" and "Every American is a man" clearly entail "Every American is mortal," while "Every man is mortal" and "Every fish is mortal" clearly do not entail "Every man is a fish," yet both are in the mood AAA. The additional factor in their forms which will enable us to distinguish them is the relative position of the terms, which can be determined uniquely by the positions of the occurrences of the middle term in particular. In the first syllogism the middle term is the subject of the first premise and the predicate of the second; in the second, it is the predicate of both premises. The ways in which the middle term can occur are four:

(i)   it may be the subject of the first premise and the predicate of the second;
(ii) it may be the predicate of both premises;
(iii) it may be the subject of both premises; and
(iv) it may be the predicate of the first and the subject of the second. (But see below for a refinement.)

Syllogisms in which the middle term occurs in these ways are said to be, respectively, in the first, second, third, and fourth **figures**. Referring to our example, we have decided that a syllogism in the mood AAA in the first figure (AAA-1) is valid, while a syllogism in the mood AAA in the second figure (AAA-2) is invalid.

We have now in fact included all the relevant factors in our characterization of the forms of syllogisms. With 64 moods, each of which may occur in each of the four figures, there are 256 syllogistic forms which we must investigate. But we must be careful not to include irrelevant differences in our characterization of syllogistic forms, and so far there is nothing to prevent us from including the obviously irrelevant matter of the order of the premises. Surely the question whether "No philosopher is an idiot" and "Some American is a philosopher" entail "Some American is not an idiot" is not distinguishable from the question whether "Some American is a philosopher" and "No philosopher is an idiot" entail "Some American is not an idiot." Yet we seem to be required to identify the form of the first as EIO-1 and that of the second as IEO-4. In order to remedy this situation, we adopt the convention that the letter indicating the form of premise containing the major term (the **major premise**) is to be listed first and the letter indicating the form of the premise containing the minor term (the **minor premise**) is to be listed second. (We may revise our above characterization of the four figures accordingly by replacing "first" by "major" and "second" by "minor" throughout.) Thus, in keeping with our aim of characterizing syllogistic forms by all and only logically relevant features, both the syllogisms just discussed will be found to have the form EIO-1.

The reader should convince himself that there is not a 257th syllogistic form waiting to be discovered, that is, that we have in fact included all and only logically relevant factors in our characterization. It is also well to recall that such factors as the possibility of treating many apparently different kinds of propositions as cp's, the possibility of paraphrasing cp's in such a way as to exchange terms for their complements or vice versa, and the possibility of constructing chains of syllogisms (called **soriteses**[4]) in which a conclusion is drawn from two premises, combined with another premise to yield another conclusion, and so on, provide indeed extensive, though by no means unlimited, resources for dealing with inferences not obviously of one of these 256 forms in terms of them.

The traditional account recognized just 24 of these syllogistic forms as carrying validity with them, as follows:[5]

[4] The word is from the Greek for "heap." Lewis Carroll [8], I, pp. 112–124, provides many humorous examples, which have often been pirated by later logicians looking for exercises.
[5] The account given here is adapted from Prior [34], pp. 114ff.

First figure: AAA-1, EAE-1, AII-1, EIO-1, AAI-1, EAO-1
Second figure: EAE-2, AEE-2, EIO-2, AOO-2, AEO-2, EAO-2
Third figure: AAI-3, AII-3, EAO-3, EIO-3, IAI-3, OAO-3
Fourth figure: AAI-4, AEE-4, IAI-4, EAO-4, EIO-4, AEO-4

There is much more to be done, however, than merely sorting out the good ones from the bad ones. In various ways systematization can be achieved. One way is to begin with a few syllogisms as fundamental and show how, by employing these together with principles of immediate inference and the square of opposition, it is possible to derive the other syllogisms. This process is called the **reduction** of the derived syllogism to the syllogism used in deriving it. Thus, if we adopt informally a proof notation like that used in the body of this book, except that we allow a main proof to begin with hypotheses, the reduction of EAE-2 to EAE-1 can be represented as follows:

1	No P is M	HP
2	Every S is M	HP
3	No M is P	simple conversion, 1
4	No S is P	EAE-1, 3, 2

Sometimes we must resort to what amounts to an NI proof in carrying out a reduction. We can give such an **indirect reduction** of AOO-2 to AAA-1 as follows:

1	Every P is M	HP
2	Some S is not M	HP
3	Every S is P	HP(NI)
4	Every P is M	B, 1
5	Every S is M	AAA-1, 4, 3
6	It's not the case that some S is not M	square of opposition, 5
7	Some S is not M	B, 2
8	It's not the case that every S is P	NI, 3—7 (6, 7)
9	Some S is not P	square of opposition, 8

Notice that the "P's," "S's," and "M's" do not always stand, respectively, for the major, minor, and middle terms of the syllogistic form to which we are appealing in carrying out the reduction.

Medieval logicians captured the tactics for carrying out reductions of this sort in a mnemonic Latin verse:

> Barbara, Celarent, Darii, Ferio-que prioris
> Cesare, Camestres, Festino, Baroco secundae
> Tertia Darapti, Disamis, Datisi, Felapton
> Bocardo, Ferison habet. Quarta insuper addit
> Bramantip, Camenes, Dimaris, Fesapo, Fresison.

The significance of the letters in these names of the valid syllogistic forms is as follows: the vowels in order give the mood names; thus Barbara is AAA and, according to what the verse itself says in Latin, first figure. The initial consonant of the name of a syllogistic form in a figure other than the first indicates that the syllogistic form in question is to be reduced to the first figure syllogistic form whose name has the same initial consonant; thus Cesare is to be reduced to Celarent. The consonants "s," "p," "c," and "m" immediately following vowels which help to characterize moods in figures other than the first have the following significance: "s" indicates that the proposition indicated by the vowel preceding it must be converted *simpliciter* in carrying out the reduction; "p" indicates that the proposition indicated by the vowel preceding it must be converted *per accidens* in carrying out the reduction; "c" indicates that the indirect method, in which the denial of the conclusion, together with the universal premise, yields the denial of the remaining premise by the syllogism to which we are reducing (whence we may infer the conclusion from the premises), must be used; "m" indicates that the order of the premises indicated by the vowels between which it occurs must be reversed. (In our representation of these methods nothing corresponds exactly to this latter instruction; we need only indicate which premise is being regarded as the major premise, which we can do by listing its number first when justifying the step in which the syllogistic form to which we are reducing is invoked.)

With these clues from the names the reader should be able to reduce any syllogistic form in a figure other than the first to a syllogistic form in the first figure. It will be observed that certain of the valid syllogistic forms are not given names in the verse. These will be found, upon inspection, to be syllogistic forms, five in number, which correspond directly to syllogistic forms which are given names, except that a particular conclusion is drawn instead of a universal one. These syllogistic forms, called **subaltern syllogistic forms**, or syllogistic forms with **weakened conclusions**, which may be named Barbari, Celaront, Cesaro, Camestrop, and Camenop, were thought to be trivially valid and not worth mentioning separately, once the syllogistic forms to which they corresponded were given. In fact, as we shall see, they turn out to be among those around which controversies concerning the doctrine of the syllogism we are here sketching revolve. It should also be noted that the directions tell us how to reduce syllogisms to the first figure rather than to some other figure or some combination of figures. There is no systematic reason why this is so; various other reductions, some of them more economical regarding basic principles, are possible. The aim of the systematization to those who originally engaged in it, however, was not only the economization of primitive principles but also the reduction of some modes of inference to others which seemed more intuitively valid or more fundamental for other reasons, and first figure syllogisms seemed, for various reasons, to fulfill these criteria particularly well.[6]

Another method of arriving systematically at the 24 valid syllogistic forms is by giving a set of statements about syllogistic forms such that a syllogistic form carries validity if and only if all those statements are true of it.

Before we can give these statements and show how they can be used to cull the good syllogistic forms from the bad, however, we must introduce another technical notion, that of the **distribution** of a term in a cp. This concept is not an easy one to grasp. Since it works in the context in which we are going to use it, it has been cut loose from an elaborate medieval set of doctrines in terms of which alone it is possible really to understand it.[7] We shall elucidate it summarily as the property a term has in a cp when there is a valid inference from

---

[6] Leibniz and others have developed other reductions. See Prior [34], pp. 119–121. On Aristotle's choice of first figure syllogisms as fundamental, see Kneale and Kneale [22], p. 76, and the references given there.

[7] See Kneale and Kneale [22], pp. 246–274, for the distinctions; and Geach [16], Chapter 1, for criticism of uses of the notion outside the context of those distinctions.

that cp to a proposition just like it, except that the name of something to which the term applies is substituted for the term. Thus, for example, "men" is distributed in "Every man is mortal" because "Every man is mortal" entails "Socrates is mortal." Conversely "mortal" is not distributed in "Every man is mortal" because "Every man is mortal" does not entail "Every man is Moby Dick" (where "Moby Dick" is the name of a mortal who happens not to be a man.) We leave it to the reader to convince himself that the application of this criterion shows that all and only universal cp's distribute their subjects, while all and only negative cp's distribute their predicates. For the use to which we are going to put the notion, it would suffice to define distribution as the property which subjects of universal cp's and predicates of negative cp's and no other terms have, without pretending to understand it any further.

We may now make four statements about syllogistic forms such that a syllogistic form carries validity if and only if all four are true of it. We may regard these as axioms, since we shall soon wish to derive some additional theorems.

A1. The middle term is distributed at least once.
A2. Any term distributed in the conclusion is distributed in the premise in which it occurs.
A3. At least one premise is affirmative.
A4. If one premise is negative, the conclusion is negative.
A5. If both premises are affirmative, the conclusion is affirmative.

The reader may wish to reflect in general on why these statements seem to give necessary and sufficient conditions of syllogistic validity; we shall regard our task rather on the analogy of that we undertook when developing a deductive system such that all and only ttt's were theorems. We shall set out to show that precisely the 24 valid syllogistic forms already listed are such that all of these four statements are true of each of them.

We could, of course, merely test them one by one, but there are ways of eliminating them in larger batches.[8] In order to do this, we must consider various related syllogistic forms together. Thus, if we consider only the arrangement of cp's as premises, there are just sixteen possible variations.

Major premise: AAAA EEEE I III OOOO
Minor premise: AEIO AEIO AEIO AE I O

[8] What follows is adapted from Cohen and Nagel [10], pp. 78–87.

Of these it can be seen that any syllogism whose premises are of the forms EE, EO, OE, or OO will be invalid since A3 is not true of them. Thus we have eliminated straight off 64 syllogistic forms, or a quarter of the total to be tested, for there are sixteen different syllogistic forms answering to each of these four descriptions, depending upon which of the four forms of cp the conclusion is and which of the four figures the syllogistic form is in.

We can eliminate 64 more at this level by proving the following theorems from our axioms:

T1: At least one premise is universal.

Proof: The proof proceeds indirectly, by assuming that both premises are particular and deriving a contradiction of one of our axioms. If the two premises are particular, they may be either (i) both O, (ii) both I, or (iii) one I and one O. (i) Under this assumption we would have an immediate contradiction of A3. (ii) Under this assumption no terms are distributed in the premises; therefore, the middle term is not distributed, which contradicts A1. (iii) Under this assumption, there will be only one distributed term in the premises. To avoid contradicting A1, this must be the middle term. But then, to avoid contradicting A2, there must be no term distributed in the conclusion. But then the conclusion cannot be negative, which results in a contradiction of A4.

T1 enables us to eliminate syllogisms with premises of the forms II, IO, and OI, as well as OO, which has already been eliminated on other grounds. We have thus eliminated 48 more. Finally, sixteen more go with the following theorem, proof of which is left to the reader:

T2: If the major premise is I, the minor is not E.

We have thus eliminated exactly half of the total number of syllogistic forms; progress gets slower from now on, and we must consider the peculiarities of each figure. We have still 32 possibilities in each figure, those with premises AA, AE, AI, AO, EA, EI, IA, and OA, and each such combination of premises with any one of the four forms of cp as conclusion. We can eliminate some of these by fours by proving some special theorems about the valid syllogisms in each figure. With regard to the first figure, we can prove the following (all remaining proofs being left to the reader):

ST1: In the first figure the minor premise is affirmative.

ST2: In the first figure the major premise is universal.

These theorems eliminate the four AE, the four AO, the four IA, and

the four OA syllogistic forms in the first figure. We are now left with
AA, AI, EA, and EI premises with any of the four forms of cp as a
possible conclusion. We must now examine these sixteen possibilities
one by one, and we shall discover that just the six forms listed earlier
as valid in the first figure are such that all our statements are true of
them.

Similar examination of the other three figures will yield the other
eighteen valid syllogistic forms. We shall simply list the special theorems
which help shorten the process of elimination in the other figures,
leaving to the reader the proofs of these theorems and the testing of
the remaining syllogistic forms against them.

ST3: In the second figure the premises differ in quality.

ST4: In the second figure the major premise is universal.

ST5: In the third figure the minor premise is affirmative.

ST6: In the third figure the conclusion is particular.

ST7: In the fourth figure, if the major premise is affirmative,
the minor premise is universal.

ST8: In the fourth figure, if either premise is negative, the major
premise is universal.

ST9: In the fourth figure, if the minor premise is affirmative,
the conclusion is particular.

The existence of exactly 24 valid forms of syllogisms has in the
past century become a matter of controversy.[9] One way to see how this
controversy arises is to consider the renditions of the forms of cp's in
terms of the apparatus of the predicate calculus given in 10.5. Let us
begin with the quite natural representation of I, "Some S is P," as
"ExKfxgx" and O, "Some S is not P," as "ExKfxNgx," letting "f"
and "g" correspond to "S" and "P," respectively. If we now accept
the view that the I and the E are contradictories, as are the A and the
O, it follows immediately that E, "No S is P," is to be rendered as
"NExKfxgx" (the denial of our rendition of the I), and the A, "Every
S is P," as "NExKfxNgx" (the denial of our rendition of the O).
Some manipulations, easily seen to be sanctioned by (i) relations
between the quantifiers and (ii) relations among the truth-functional
constants, quickly reveal these renditions to be equivalent to

---

[9] See Prior [34], pp. 164ff., for an historical account. See also the selections by
Brentano and Strawson (Selections 18 and 19) in Iseminger [21].

"AxCfxNgx" for the E and "AxCfxgx" for the A, whence the doctrine which results is known as the **hypothetical interpretation** of the universal cp's.

We have set up our interpretations of the cp's precisely so as to maintain the contradictory relationships among them, but what happens to the other relationships of the square of opposition? The key fact, from which all the other consequences can be seen to follow, is that relations of subalternation no longer hold. We could see this by trying to prove, for example, "CAxCfxgxExKfxgx," which turns out not to be provable. Another way to see this is to reflect that, if we interpret "Ex" as standing for "there exists," an A proposition will be true if there is nothing to which the predicate for which "f" is a stand-in applies, while the corresponding I proposition, which asserts that there *is* something to which the predicate for which "f" is a stand-in applies, will be false under the same conditions. This fact is often summarized by saying that, under the interpretations of the cp's we are now considering the A and E do not have **existential import**, while the I and O do. It follows, of course, from the fact that there is a situation in which the A is true and its corresponding I false that the A can no longer be said to entail the corresponding I, and a similar argument would reveal that the E can no longer be said to entail the corresponding O.

What happens to our doctrine of cp's on this principle? Just insofar as other relations on the square of opposition were shown to be related to subalternation, they will also now fail. We can extend the argument to say, in general, that no particular cp (with existential import) follows from premises which include only universal cp's (without existential import). From this it follows that *per accidens* modes of immediate inference are invalidated, that the five "trivial" subaltern syllogistic forms are invalidated, and that four other syllogistic forms (AAI-3, EAO-3, AAI-4, and EAO-4, called syllogistic forms with **strengthened premises** because a similar syllogistic form with an allegedly "weaker" particular premise replacing one of the allegedly "stronger" universal premises is valid) are also invalidated. We are thus left with just fifteen valid syllogistic forms.

The methods for determining valid syllogistic forms already discussed can be revised to take account of this new development. As regards the doctrine of reduction, we have only to strike the two subaltern syllogisms from our list of "given" first figure syllogisms and eliminate *per accidens* modes of immediate inference from the list of operations permissible in reducing one syllogistic form to another. As regards our statements about syllogistic forms, we have only to add a fifth:

A6. If the conclusion is particular, at least one of the premises is particular.

The reader is left to work out these revisions in detail if he so desires.

There is another way of testing syllogistic forms for validity, however, which involves, as it is usually presented, an immediate commitment to the hypothetical interpretation of the universal cp's, and this is the so-called **Venn diagram** technique.[10] In this method the forms of the cp's are represented by appropriate maneuvers with two intersecting circles, representing the predicates for which "f" and "g" are stand-ins.[11] Let us consider the A first, concentrating on that version of our current interpretation which makes A propositions into explicit denials of existential statements, "NExKfxNgx." If we let an asterisk in the intersection of the circles represent something to which both "f" and "g" apply, and asterisks in the other areas represent things to which "f" but not "g" and "g" but not "f" apply, respectively, and if, analogously, we adopt the convention of shading out an area to show that there is nothing to which the associated predicate or predicates apply, the A form appears diagrammatically as follows:

A: NExKfxNgx

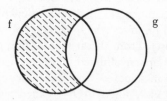

[10] Devised by the English logician John Venn. See Kneale and Kneale [22], pp. 420ff. Other diagrammatic techniques, for this and other parts of logic, have been devised by, among others, Euler (see Kneale and Kneale [22], pp. 349ff.), Carroll [8], and Peirce [31], 4.394ff.

[11] If we wished to extend the technique to deal with inferences involving complements, we would have to surround the circles with a square representing the so-called "universe of discourse" (those things to which "f" or "g" could conceivably apply.) See Cohen and Nagel [10], pp. 39–41.

Similarly the E:

E: NExKfxgx

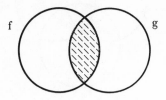

The I may be diagrammed thus:

I: ExKfxgx

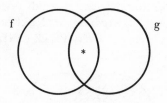

Finally, the O appears as follows:

O: ExKfxNgx

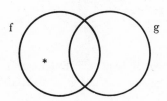

These diagrams show vividly the existential import of the A and E and the lack of existential import of the I and O on the hypothetical interpretation.

In order to diagram a syllogism, which has three terms, we shall require three circles arranged so as to cover all the possible combinations of the predicates applying or not, thus:

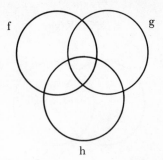

To test a syllogistic form by this method, we have only to represent the forms of both premises simultaneously on the diagram and see whether, in the process, we have represented the form of the conclusion. If and only if we have, the syllogism is valid. (Why is this intuitively plausible?) Thus AAA-1, "Every h is g" ("NExKhxNgx") and "Every f is h" ("NExKfxNhx") entail "Every f is g" ("NExKfxNgx"):

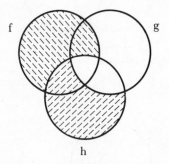

Or again, EIO-1, "No h is g" ("NExKhxgx") and "Some f is h" ("ExKfxhx") entail "Some f is not g" ("ExKfxNgx"):

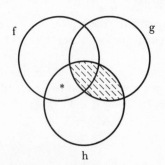

In the first example the appropriate area simply gets shaded out in the process of diagramming the premises. In the second, since we cannot put the asterisk where we have already shaded (why not?), we are forced to put the asterisk representing the form of the minor premise where it will also represent the form of the conclusion. It can be seen from this example that, where we have one universal premise and one particular premise, it is necessary to diagram the form of the universal premise first; otherwise, we shall not know in which of two possible areas to put the asterisk. (If this should happen, one may put the asterisk on the line, being careful not to assume that it is on one side of the line rather than another unless shading of one side of the line should make it topple into one area or the other.) The reader is left to see that just the required fifteen syllogistic forms are valid by this test.

The kind of reasoning we go through in validating syllogistic forms by the Venn diagram test can be seen more clearly if we let metavariables replace wff's representing the forms of propositions which assert the existence of things to which the predicates corresponding to the distinct areas of the diagram apply, thus:[12]

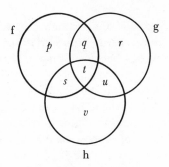

p replaces "ExKfxKNgxNhx."
q replaces "ExKKfxgxNhx."
r replaces "ExKgxKNfxNhx."
s replaces "ExKKfxhxNgx."
t replaces "ExKKfxgxhx."
u replaces "ExKKgxhxNfx."
v replaces "ExKhxKNfxNgx."

[12] See Prior [34], pp. 172ff.

Diagramming a proposition of the form "Every h is g," which consists of shading the sections of the diagram associated with the propositions replaced by *s* and *v* above, may then be represented as denying *s* and denying *v*. (Why?) ("NExKhxNgx," the proposed original representation of "Every h is g," may be shown, by a rather complicated proof, to be equivalent to "KNExKKfxhxNgxNExKhxKNfxNgx," which according to the above table is the equivalent of denying *s* and denying *v*; that is, it is equivalent to KN*s*N*v*.) Similarly, "Every f is h" may be represented as KN*p*N*q*, and the conclusion which follows in AAA-1, "Every f is g," as KN*p*N*s*. The equivalence of the formula for which one of these expressions stands and the original representation of the associated proposition in the predicate calculus may also be proved here as well. Given these representations, the question of the validity of AAA-1 now amounts to the question whether we can prove CKKN*s*N*v*KN*p*N*q*KN*p*N*s*, which we can prove very easily.

To represent a particular cp, we resort to the disjunction of the two propositions associated in the above diagram with the areas in one of which an asterisk would have to be found in a Venn diagram representing the cp. Thus, for example, "Some f is h" appears as A*st*, and so on, and the validity of EIO-1 reduces to the provability of CKKN*t*N*u*A*st*A*sp*.

These representations of the reasoning involved show how the diagrams do in fact represent the appropriate propositions (here we refer to the equivalence of what, for example, A*st* replaces, according to the above table, to "ExKfxgx"). They also show how, once the propositions are represented on the diagram, arguing that the automatic diagramming of the conclusion in the process of diagramming the premises shows the validity of the inference is just a matter of appealing to familiar facts of propositional logic. (On this latter question recall also our use of familiar kinds of propositional arguments in conducting reductions.) While this does not show that, in any significant sense, syllogistic logic is reducible to propositional logic (for the relation of our chosen *p*'s and *q*'s to the wff's they replace is very much a matter of predicate logic), it does belie any claim of syllogistic logic to be "basic." Syllogistic logic can here be seen very clearly to involve various kinds of inference which are not themselves part of the theory of the syllogism or of the logic of categorical propositions at all but on which many of the moves in the theory of the syllogism depend for their validity.

We have traced the consequences of adopting the hypothetical interpretation of universal cp's. We shall not here discuss the question of which of the two doctrines of cp's we discussed is the more adequate representation of the entailments in which propositions of this kind are involved. Several things have to be kept in mind in any such discussion, however. First, the consequences we have traced of adopting the hypothetical interpretation flow as much from our rendition of cp's in terms of the apparatus of the predicate calculus as they do from the properties of the quantifiers. If we regard the syllogistic system as originally sketched as worth saving and are also committed to using the quantificational apparatus as far as possible, we can look for other ways of rendering the cp's in terms of that apparatus. As a start, we might try simply tacking on something to give the A and the E existential import, thus:

A: KNExKfxNgxExfx.
E: KNExKfxgxExfx.

This interpretation, called the **existential interpretation** of the A and the E, reinstates the relations of subalternation (why?) and with them the nine recently abandoned syllogistic forms, but, as we might expect, tinkering one place has consequences elsewhere. The standard contradictory relationships, which seem as desirable to maintain as anything, will disappear, for example. (Why?) With further tinkering it is possible to express the cp's in the quantificational notation in such a way that all the original principles sanctioned by the traditional system we outlined hold good, but this move has the apparently disastrous consequence of robbing the I and the O of existential import. We shall not record this adventure in detail, but at this point the reader, if he is convinced of the justness of the traditional system, may begin to doubt the adequacy of the quantificational apparatus to represent cp's accurately.[13]

[13] For an account of this adventure, after which the moral just hinted at is drawn, see Strawson [45], pp. 163–179.

Appendix B: OTHER NOTATIONS

Because of the many references to other works in this book, it will be helpful to compare the notation used here with other systems of notation in common use. These other notations are due to Peano and have been common since the publication of Whitehead and Russell [49]. To facilitate comparison, we give here one possible set of formation rules involving the Peano-style notation. Proposition stand-ins and name variables are unchanged from our Polish notation, but predicate stand-ins are the Greek "ϕ," "ψ," etc.

(i) A proposition stand-in is a wff.

(ii) An n-placed predicate stand-in followed by n occurrences of name variables is a wff.

(iii) If p is a wff, then $\sim(p)$, $\Box(p)$, $\Diamond(p)$, $(\exists x)(p)$, and $(x)(p)$ are wff's.

(iv) If p and q are wff's, then $(p) \cdot (q)$, $(p) \vee (q)$, $(p) \supset (q)$, $(p) \equiv (q)$, $(p) \prec (q)$, and $(p) \equiv\!\!\equiv (q)$ are wff's.

(v) There are no wff's other than those specified in (i)—(iv).

These symbols and the symbols in Polish notation may be correlated as follows:

"N" is "$\sim$." (A straight line "—" over the entire wff to which the symbol applies, for example, "$\overline{(p) \vee (q)}$," is sometimes used.

"L" is "$\Box$."

"M" is "$\Diamond$."

"Ex" is "$(\exists x)$."

"Ax" is "(x)." ("$(\forall x)$" is sometimes used.)

"K" is "$\cdot$." ("&," "$\wedge$," and the simple adjunction of the wff's joined are sometimes used.)

"A" is "$\vee$." (Simple adjunction is also sometimes used here.)

"C" is "$\supset$." ("$\rightarrow$" is sometimes used.)

"E" is "$\equiv$."

"C'" is "$\prec$."

"E'" is "$\equiv\!\!\equiv$."

$$
\begin{array}{c|c|l}
\cdot & \cdot & \\
n & \mathrm{N}p & \mathrm{NI},\ k\text{---}m\ (l,\ m) \\
\cdot & \cdot & \\
\cdot & \cdot &
\end{array}
$$

or as above with steps l and m in reverse order.

$$
\text{(NNE)}\quad
\begin{array}{c|l}
\cdot & \cdot \\
\cdot & \cdot \\
m & \mathrm{NN}p \qquad \mathrm{R}i \\
\cdot & \cdot \\
\cdot & \cdot \\
n & p \qquad\quad \mathrm{NNE},\ m \\
\cdot & \cdot \\
\cdot & \cdot
\end{array}
$$

$$
\text{(CI)}\quad
\begin{array}{c|l}
\cdot & \cdot \\
\cdot & \cdot \\
l & p \qquad\quad \mathrm{HP(CI)} \\
\cdot & \cdot \\
\cdot & \cdot \\
\cdot & \cdot \\
m & q \qquad\quad \mathrm{R}i \\
\cdot & \cdot \\
\cdot & \cdot \\
n & \mathrm{C}pq \qquad \mathrm{CI},\ l\text{---}m \\
\cdot & \cdot \\
\cdot & \cdot
\end{array}
$$

(CE)

l	Cpq	Ri
m	p	Rj
n	q	CE, l, m

or as above with steps l and m in reverse order.

Rule of Borrowing

A step preceding a subordinate proof and occurring in a proof to which that subordinate proof is subordinate may be written down in that subordinate proof.

Definitions

D1. Apq and $CNpq$ are equivalent by definition.
D2. Kpq and $NCpNq$ are equivalent by definition.
D3. Epq and $NCCpqNCqp$ are equivalent by definition.

Rule of Definitional Replacement

Given a step p, it is permissible to write down a step q, where q is the result of substituting for any (proper or improper) part of p which is itself a wff another wff equivalent to that part according to D1—D3.

Derived Introduction and Elimination Rules

(AI)

l	p	Ri
m	Apq	AI, l

$\cdot$ | $\cdot$ $\cdot$

$\cdot$ | $\cdot$ $\cdot$

n | Aqp AI, l

$\cdot$ | $\cdot$ $\cdot$

$\cdot$ | $\cdot$ $\cdot$

(AE) $\cdot$ | $\cdot$ $\cdot$

$\cdot$ | $\cdot$ $\cdot$

j | Apq Rg

$\cdot$ | $\cdot$ $\cdot$

$\cdot$ | $\cdot$ $\cdot$

k | p HP(AE)

$\cdot$ | $\cdot$ $\cdot$

$\cdot$ | $\cdot$ $\cdot$

$\cdot$ | $\cdot$ $\cdot$

l | r Rh

$\cdot$ | $\cdot$ $\cdot$

$\cdot$ | $\cdot$ $\cdot$

m | q HP(AE)

$\cdot$ | $\cdot$ $\cdot$

$\cdot$ | $\cdot$ $\cdot$

$\cdot$ | $\cdot$ $\cdot$

n | r Ri

$\cdot$ | $\cdot$ $\cdot$

$\cdot$ | $\cdot$ $\cdot$

o | r AE, j, k—l, m—n

$\cdot$ | $\cdot$ $\cdot$

$\cdot$ | $\cdot$ $\cdot$

or as above with proofs k—l and m—n in reverse order.

(KI)

	·	·
	·	·
k	p	Ri
	·	·
	·	·
l	q	Rj
	·	·
	·	·
m	Kpq	KI, k, l
	·	·
	·	·
n	Kqp	KI, k, l
	·	·
	·	·

(KE)

	·	·
	·	·
l	Kpq	Ri
	·	·
	·	·
m	p	KE, l
	·	·
	·	·
n	q	KE, l
	·	·
	·	·

(EI)

	·	·
	·	·
k	p	HP(EI)
	·	

$$
\begin{array}{r|l|l}
 & \cdot \quad \Big| \quad \cdot & \cdot \\
 & \cdot \quad \Big| \quad \cdot & \cdot \\
l & \quad \Big| \quad q & \mathrm{R}i \\
 & \cdot \quad \Big| & \cdot \\
 & \cdot \quad \Big| & \cdot \\
m & \quad \Big| \quad q & \mathrm{HP(EI)} \\
 & \cdot \quad \Big| & \cdot \\
 & \cdot \quad \Big| \quad \cdot & \cdot \\
 & \cdot \quad \Big| \quad \cdot & \cdot \\
n & \quad \Big| \quad p & \mathrm{R}j \\
 & \cdot \quad \Big| & \cdot \\
 & \cdot \quad \Big| & \cdot \\
o & \mathrm{E}pq & \mathrm{EI},\ k\!-\!l,\ m\!-\!n \\
 & \cdot & \cdot \\
 & \cdot & \cdot
\end{array}
$$

or as above with proofs k—l and m—n in reverse order.

$$
\text{(EE)}
\begin{array}{r|l|l}
 & \cdot \quad \Big| & \cdot \\
 & \cdot \quad \Big| & \cdot \\
l & \mathrm{E}pq & \mathrm{R}i \\
 & \cdot \quad \Big| & \cdot \\
 & \cdot \quad \Big| & \cdot \\
m & p & \mathrm{R}j \\
 & \cdot \quad \Big| & \cdot \\
 & \cdot \quad \Big| & \cdot \\
n & q & \mathrm{EE},\ l,\ m \\
 & \cdot \quad \Big| & \cdot \\
 & \cdot \quad \Big| & \cdot
\end{array}
$$

also:

.	.	.
.	.	.
l	Epq	Ri
.	.	.
.	.	.
m	q	Rj
.	.	.
.	.	.
n	p	EE, l, m
.	.	.
.	.	.

or as either of the above with steps l and m in reverse order.

II.   MODAL PROPOSITIONAL CALCULUS

Vocabulary

   (i)   and (ii) as in the propositional calculus.
   (iii) Modal constants, "L," "M," "C'," and "E'."

Formation Rules

   (i)—(iii) as in the propositional calculus.
   (iv) If p is a wff, then Lp and Mp are wff's.
   (v) If p and q are wff's, then C'pq and E'pq are wff's.
   (vi) There are no wff's other than those specified in (i)—(v).

Underived Introduction and Elimination Rules

As in the propositional calculus plus the following additions:

(LI)

.	.	.
.	.	.
l	L	.
.	.	.
.	.	.

```
  m |  | p              Ri
    ·  |  ·              ·
    ·  |  ·              ·
  n |  Lp               LI, l—m
    ·  |  ·              ·
    ·  |  ·              ·
(LE) ·  |  ·             ·
    ·  |  ·              ·
  m |  Lp               ·
    ·  |  ·              ·
    ·  |  ·              ·
  n |  p                LE, m
    ·  |  ·              ·
    ·  |  ·              ·
```

Rule of Borrowing

As in the propositional calculus, except that if the subordinate proof into which the step is being borrowed is a strict proof, or is subordinate to a strict proof which is subordinate to the proof in which the step occurs, the step being borrowed must be of one of the following forms: Lp, $NMNp$, $C'pq$, $E'pq$.

Definitions

D1—D3 as in the propositional calculus, plus the following additions:

D4. Mp and $NLNp$ are equivalent by definition.

D5. $C'pq$ and $LCpq$ are equivalent by definition.

D6. $E'pq$ and $NCLCpqNLCqp$ are equivalent by definition.

Rule of Definitional Replacement

As in the propositional calculus, except change "D1—D3" to "D1—D6."

Derived Introduction and Elimination Rules

As in the propositional calculus, plus the following additions:

(MI)

·	·	·
·	·	·
m	p	Ri
·	·	·
·	·	·
n	Mp	MI, m
·	·	·
·	·	·

(ME)

·	·	·
·	·	·
k	Mp	Ri
·	·	·
·	·	·
l	L p	HP(ME)
·	·	·
·	·	·
·	·	·
m	q	Rj
·	·	·
·	·	·
n	Mq	ME, k, l—m
·	·	·
·	·	·

(C'I)

	·	·
	·	·
l	L⌐ p	HP(C'I)
	·	·
	·	·
	·	·
m	q	Ri
	·	·
	·	·
n	C'pq	C'I, l—m
	·	·
	·	·

(C'E)

	·	·
	·	·
l	C'pq	Ri
	·	·
	·	·
m	Lp	Rj
	·	·
	·	·
n	Lq	C'E, l, m
	·	·
	·	·

also:

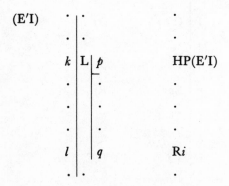

.	.	.
.	.	.
l	C'pq	Ri
.	.	.
.	.	.
m	p	Rj
.	.	.
.	.	.
n	q	C'E, l, m
.	.	.
.	.	.

or as either of the above with steps l and m in reverse order.

(E'I)

.	.	.
.	.	.
k	L p	HP(E'I)
.	.	.
.	.	.
.	.	.
l	q	Ri
.	.	.

	·	·	·
m	L	q	HP(E′I)
	·	·	·
	·	·	·
	·	·	·
n		p	Rj
	·	·	·
	·	·	·
o	E′pq		E′I, k—l, m—n
	·	·	·
	·	·	·

or as above with proofs k—l and m—n in reverse order.

(E′E)

·	·	·
·	·	·
l	E′pq	Ri
·	·	·
·	·	·
m	Lp	Rj
·	·	·
·	·	·
n	Lq	E′E, l, m
·	·	·
·	·	·

also:

.	.	.
.	.	.
l	E'pq	Ri
.	.	.
.	.	.
m	Lq	Rj
.	.	.
.	.	.
n	Lp	E'E, l, m
.	.	.
.	.	.

also:

.	.	.
.	.	.
l	E'pq	Ri
.	.	.
.	.	.
m	p	Rj
.	.	.
.	.	.
n	q	E'E, l, m
.	.	.
.	.	.

also:

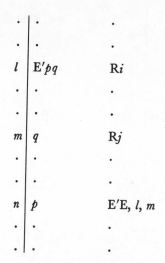

or as any of the above with steps l and m in reverse order.

III. PREDICATE CALCULUS

Vocabulary

  (i) and (ii) as in the propositional calculus.
 (iii) Predicate stand-ins, "f," "g," "h," etc.
 (iv) Name variables, "x," "y," "z," etc.
  (v) Quantifiers, "Ax," "Ay," "Az," etc. and "Ex," "Ey," "Ez," etc.

Formation Rules

  (i)—(iii) as in the propositional calculus.
 (iv) An n-placed predicate stand-in followed by n occurrences of name variables is a wff.
  (v) If p is a wff, then Axp, Ayp, Azp, etc., and Exp, Eyp, Ezp, etc., are wff's.
 (vi) There are no wff's other than those specified in (i)—(v).

Underived Introduction and Elimination Rules

As in the propositional calculus, plus the following additions:

(AxI)

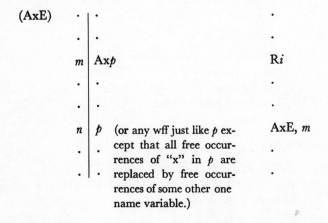

l	x	·
m	p	Ri
n	Axp	AxI, l—m

or as above with "y's" replacing all the "x's," or "z's" replacing all the "x's," etc.

(AxE)

m	Axp	Ri
n	p (or any wff just like p except that all free occurrences of "x" in p are replaced by free occurrences of some other one name variable.)	AxE, m

or as above with "y's" replacing all the "x's," or "z's" replacing all the "x's," etc.

Rule of Borrowing

As in the propositional calculus, except that if the subordinate proof into which the step is being borrowed is general with respect to a name variable, or is subordinate to a proof or proofs general with respect to name variables, which proof or proofs are subordinate to the proof in which the step occurs, the step being borrowed must contain no free occurrences of any of the name variables with respect to which the proof into which the step is being borrowed, or any proof to which that proof is subordinate and which is subordinate to the proof in which that step occurs, is general.

Definitions

D1—D3 as in the propositional calculus, plus the following addition:

D7. Ex*p* and NAxN*p* are equivalent by definition (also Ey*p* and NAyN*p*, Ez*p* and NAzN*p*, etc.)

Rule of Definitional Replacement

As in the propositional calculus, except replace "D1—D3" with "D1—D3, and D7."

Derived Introduction and Elimination Rules

As in the propositional calculus, with the following additions:

(ExI)

	·	·	·
	·	·	·
m	*p*	(or any wff just like *p* except that all free occurrences of "x" in *p* are replaced by free occurrences of some other one	R*i*
	·		·
	·		·
n	Ex*p*	name variable.)	ExI, *m*
	·		·
	·		·

or as above with "y's" replacing all the "x's," or "z's" replacing all the "x's," etc.

(ExE)	·	·		·
	·	·		·
k	Exp			Ri
	·	·		·
	·	·		·
l	x	p		HP(ExE)
	·	·		·
	·	·		·
	·	·		·
m		q	(where q contains no free occurrences of "x.")	Rj
	·	·		·
	·	·		·
n	q			ExE, k, l—m
	·	·		·
	·	·		·

or as above with "y's" replacing all the "x's," or "z's" replacing all the "x's," etc.

BIBLIOGRAPHY

The following items are identified by author or editor and by number in footnotes which refer to them in the course of the book.

[1] Ammerman, Robert R., *Classics of Analytic Philosophy* (New York, McGraw-Hill, 1965).

[2] Anderson, Alan Ross, and Nuel D. Belnap, Jr., "The Pure Calculus of Entailment," *The Journal of Symbolic Logic*, Vol. 27, No. 1 (March, 1962), pp. 19–52.

[3] Anderson, John M., and Henry W. Johnstone, Jr., *Natural Deduction* (Belmont, Calif., Wadsworth, 1962).

[4] Austin, J. L., *Sense and Sensibilia* (Oxford, Oxford University Press, 1962).

[5] Beardsley, Monroe C., *Practical Logic* (Englewood Cliffs, N. J., Prentice-Hall, 1950).

[6] Benacerraf, Paul, and Hilary Putnam, *Philosophy of Mathematics: Selected Readings* (Englewood Cliffs, N. J., Prentice-Hall, 1964).

[7] Bird, Otto, *Syllogistic and Its Extentions* (Englewood Cliffs, N. J., Prentice-Hall, 1964).

[8] Carroll, Lewis, *Symbolic Logic* and *The Game of Logic* (New York, Dover, 1958).

[9] Clark, Romane, and Paul Welsh, *Introduction to Logic* (Princeton, N. J., Van Nostrand, 1962).

[10] Cohen, Morris R., and Ernest Nagel, *An Introduction to Logic* (New York, Harcourt, Brace & World, 1962).

[11] Copi, Irving M., and James A. Gould, *Readings on Logic* (New York, Macmillan, 1964).

[12] Donagan, Alan, "Universals and Metaphysical Realism," *The Monist*, Vol. 47, No. 2 (January, 1963), pp. 211–246.

[13] Feigl, Herbert, and Wilfrid Sellars, *Readings in Philosophical Analysis* (New York, Appleton-Century-Crofts, 1949).

[14] Fitch, Frederic Brenton, *Symbolic Logic* (New York, Ronald, 1952).

[15] Foster, Marguerite H., and Michael L. Martin, *Probability, Confirmation, and Simplicity* (New York, Odyssey, 1966).

[16] Geach, Peter Thomas, *Reference and Generality* (Ithaca, N. Y., Cornell University Press, 1962).

[17] Gentzen, Gerhard, "Investigations into Logical Deduction," *American Philosophical Quarterly*, Vol. 1, No. 4 (October, 1964), pp. 288–306; Vol. 2, No. 3 (July, 1965), pp. 204–218.

[18] Harrah, David, "A Logic of Questions and Answers," *Philosophy of Science*, Vol. 28, No. 1 (January, 1961), pp. 40–46.

[19] Hintikka, Jaakko, *Knowledge and Belief* (Ithaca, N. Y., Cornell University Press, 1962).

[20] Hilbert, D., and W. Ackermann, *Principles of Mathematical Logic* (New York, Chelsea, 1950).

[21] Iseminger, Gary, *Logic and Philosophy: Selected Readings* (New York, Appleton-Century-Crofts, 1968).

[22] Kneale, William, and Martha Kneale, *The Development of Logic* (London, Oxford University Press, 1962).

[23] Lewis, Clarence Irving, and Cooper Harold Langford, *Symbolic Logic* (New York, Dover, 1959).

[24] Łukasiewicz, Jan, *Aristotle's Syllogistic from the Standpoint of Modern Formal Logic* (London, Oxford University Press, 1957).

[25] Malcolm, Norman, *Knowledge and Certainty* (Englewood Cliffs, N. J., Prentice-Hall, 1963).

[26] Mill, John Stuart, *Philosophy of Scientific Method* (New York, Hafner, 1950).

[27] Mitchell, David, *An Introduction to Logic* (London, Hutchinson, 1962).

[28] Moore, G. E., *Philosophical Studies* (London, Routledge, 1922).

[29] Nidditch, P. H., *Propositional Calculus* (New York, Dover, 1962).

[30] Parker, Francis H., and Henry B. Veatch, *Logic as a Human Instrument* (New York, Harper, 1959).

[31] Peirce, Charles Sanders, *Collected Papers* (Cambridge, Mass., Harvard University Press, 1931–1935).

[32] Pitcher, George, *The Philosophy of Wittgenstein* (Englewood Cliffs, N. J., Prentice-Hall, 1964).

[33] Pitcher, George, *Truth* (Englewood Cliffs, N. J., Prentice-Hall, 1964).

[34] Prior, A. N., *Formal Logic* (London, Oxford University Press, 1962).

[35] Quine, Willard Van Orman, *Mathematical Logic* (Cambridge, Mass., Harvard University Press, 1951).

[36] Quine, Willard Van Orman, *Methods of Logic* (New York, Holt, Rinehart and Winston, 1959).

[37] Quine, Willard Van Orman, *From a Logical Point of View* (Cambridge, Mass., Harvard University Press, 1961).

[38] Quine, Willard Van Orman, *Word and Object* (Cambridge, Mass., M.I.T. Press, 1960).

[39] Rescher, Nicholas, *The Logic of Commands* (New York, Dover, 1966).

[40] Russell, Bertrand, *The Problems of Philosophy* (New York, Oxford University Press, 1959).

[41] Russell, Bertrand, *Our Knowledge of the External World* (New York, Mentor, 1960).

[42] Russell, Bertrand, *An Inquiry into Meaning and Truth* (Baltimore, Penguin, 1962).

[43] Russell, Bertrand, *A History of Western Philosophy* (New York, Simon and Schuster, 1945).

[44] Ryle, Gilbert, *The Concept of Mind* (London, Hutchinson, 1949).

[45] Strawson, P. F., *Introduction to Logical Theory* (London, Methuen, 1952).

[46] Suppes, Patrick, *Introduction to Logic* (Princeton, N. J., Van Nostrand, 1957).

[47] Taylor, Paul W., *The Moral Judgment: Readings in Contemporary Metaethics* (Englewood Cliffs, N. J., Prentice-Hall, 1963).

[48] Veatch, Henry Babcock, *Intentional Logic* (New Haven, Conn., Yale University Press, 1952).

[49] Whitehead, Alfred North, and Bertrand Russell, *Principia Mathematica to *56* (London, Cambridge University Press, 1962).

[50] Wittgenstein, Ludwig, *Tractatus Logico-Philosophicus* (London, Routledge, 1961).

[51] Wittgenstein, Ludwig, *Philosophical Investigations* (New York, Macmillan, 1953).

INDEX

A (connective), 24, 28f., 41
A (proposition), 140
A1 (axiom), 47, 77
A2 (axiom), 47, 77
A3 (axiom), 47, 77
A4 (axiom), 47, 77
A5 (axiom), 47, 77
Ackermann, W., 23n, 77n, 83n, 112n, 137n, 178
AE (rule), 64, 74f., 163
Affirmative (proposition), 139
AI (rule), 64, 75, 162f.
All, 114, 134
Ammerman, Robert R., 12n, 116n, 177
And, 24
Anderson, Alan Ross, 78n, 105n, 106n, 177
Anderson, John M., 51n, 177
Antecedent, 19f.
Any, 114
Argument, 2
Aristotle, 6n, 133n, 139, 147n
Assertion, 1ff.
Attributive tie, 113
Austin, J. L., 2n, 177
Ax (constant), 111
AxE (rule), 120ff., 127, 174
AxI (rule), 123ff., 174
Axiom, 45
Axiom schema, 47

B (rule of borrowing), 58, 72, 77, 162, 167, 175
Basis (clause of recusive definition), 79
Beardsley, Monroe, C., 3n, 177
Belnap, Nuel D., Jr., 78n, 105n, 106n, 177
Benacerraf, Paul, 12n, 137n, 177
Bird, Otto, 142n, 177
Boolean algebra, 37n
Bound (occurrence of name variable), 111

Brentano, Franz, 150n
Brouwer, L. E. J., 12n

C (connective), 24, 28f., 54ff., 91ff., 101, 103, 106
C' (connective), 101ff.
Carroll, Lewis (C. L. Dodgson), 24n, 144n, 152n, 177
Categorical proposition (cp), 115, 133ff., 139ff.
Category, 5n
CE (rule), 59, 72, 77, 162
C'E (rule), 101f., 169f.
Chisholm, Roderick, 43n
CI (rule), 55, 72, 77, 161
C'I (rule), 102, 169
Clark, Romane, 68n, 177
Class, 137
Cohen, L. J., 136n
Cohen, Morris R., 148n, 152n, 177
Complement, 141, 152n
Completeness, 77, 83ff.
    absolute, 88
    relative, 89
Component proposition, 14
Concepts, 13, 15f.
Conclusion, 142
Conditional, 19ff., 40, 42
    open, 40, 115
Conjunctive normal form (cnf), 83ff.
Connection (and "if . . . then"), 40, 42
Consequent, 19ff.
Consistency, 77, 81ff.
    absolute, 88f.
    relative, 89f.
Constants, logical, 94
Content, 13ff.
Contradictory, 142
Contraposition, 141
Contrary, 142
Converse, 140

Name, 108
Name variable, 108
NE (rule), 72
Necessity, 93ff.
Negative (proposition), 139
NI (rule), 61f., 72, 77, 160f.
Nidditch, P. H., 48n, 178
NNE (rule), 61f., 77, 161
NNI (rule), 71
Not, 24
N-placed predicate stand-in, 110

O (proposition), 140
Obversion, 141
Ontological argument, 135n
Or, 24, 29f., 41
Outermost proof, 79

Pap, Arthur, 13n
Paradoxes
  of material implication, 91
  of strict implication, 105
Paraphrase, 38ff., 144
Parker, Francis H., 140n, 142n, 178
Particular (proposition), 139
Peano, G., 158
Peirce, Charles Sanders, 2n, 6n, 27n, 36n, 152n, 178
Pitcher, George, 6n, 9n, 11n, 43n, 110n, 178
Plato, 108
Polish notation, 24n, 158
Possibility, 98ff.
Post, E. L., 90n
Predicate, 108, 113f., 135
  of cp, 140
Predicate calculus, 113, 119ff.
Predicate stand-in, 109
Premise, 142
Primitive notions, 37
Prior, A. N., 94n, 124n, 137n, 144n, 147n, 150n, 155n, 178
Proof, 45, 48, 56
Proposition, 5ff.
  simple, 14, 107ff.
  complex, 14
Proposition stand-in, 24

Propositional calculus, 45ff., 160ff.
Propositional connective, 25
Putnam, Hilary, 12n, 137n, 177

Quality (of a cp), 139
Quantifiers, 110ff.
Quantity (of a cp), 139
Quasi-proof, 79
Quine, Willard Van Orman, 8n, 12n, 15n, 16n, 27n, 33n, 35n, 77n, 106n, 108n, 112n, 114n, 116n, 117n, 136n, 137n, 178

R1 (rule), 48, 77ff.
R2 (rule), 48, 77, 79
Reading (of a theorem), 92f., 101
Reduction, 145f., 151f.
Relational predicate, 109
Rescher, Nicholas, 7n, 178
Russell, Bertrand, 2n, 12n, 13n, 21n, 38n, 108n, 109n, 116n, 133n, 135n, 137n, 142n, 158, 178
Ryle, Gilbert, 5n, 135n, 179

S (connective), 36
S4 (system), 103n
Scope (of quantifier), 111
Sellars, Wilfrid, 13n, 43n, 116n, 135n, 177
Sentence, 1, 6
Sentence-token, 6ff.
Sentence-type, 6ff., 38f.
Set, 137
Sheffer, H. M., 36n
Some, 107, 111, 114, 134, 136, 140
Sorites, 144
Specification, 110
Square of opposition, 133, 142
Statement, 9
Strawson, P. F., 6n, 9n, 12n, 16n, 37n, 43n, 116n, 133n, 150n, 157n, 179
Subalternation, 142
Subcontrariety, 142
Subject
  of sentence, 108
  of cp, 140